THE ART OF HEALING

François Gautier is a French journalist who has been the South Asia correspondent for the largest French daily, *Le Figaro*, for over ten years. He is the author of a number of books and has written regular columns for Indian publications such as *Outlook* and the *Indian Express*.

Namrita Gautier is a textile designer and an Art of Living teacher who writes books for children.

THE ART OF HEALING

Pranayama: The Breath of Life

Namrita Gautier and François Gautier

HarperCollins *Publishers* India
a joint venture with

New Delhi

First published in India in 2010 by
HarperCollins *Publishers* India
a joint venture with
The India Today Group

ISBN: 978-81-7223-808-7

2 4 6 8 10 9 7 5 3

Photographs by courtesy of The Art of Living International Centre, Bangalore, India

HarperCollins *Publishers*
A-53, Sector 57, Noida 201301, India
77-85 Fulham Palace Road, London W6 8JB, United Kingdom
Hazelton Lanes, 55 Avenue Road, Suite 2900, Toronto, Ontario M5R 3L2
and 1995 Markham Road, Scarborough, Ontario M1B 5M8, Canada
25 Ryde Road, Pymble, Sydney, NSW 2073, Australia
31 View Road, Glenfield, Auckland 10, New Zealand
10 East 53rd Street, New York NY 10022, USA

Typeset in 11/13.5 Sabon
InoSoft Systems

Printed and bound at
Thomson Press (India) Ltd.

To the One who has uplifted our lives

Contents

HEALING THE BODY   39

HEALING THE MIND   75

CONFLICT RESOLUTION   95

Prologue

It was *brahma muhurtam*, the hour when the gods awake. Across the vast expanse of Bangalore's Jakkur airfield, three million people sat perfectly still upon silence's marge. One could almost feel the hearts and minds of those souls rise heavenwards like a giant aspiration, the prayer of all humanity willing itself to be freed from its yoke.

Borders faded as millions came together from over 150 countries to celebrate His Holiness Sri Sri Ravi Shankar's message of *Vasudhaiva Kutumbakam* or 'one world family' on the world's largest stage, managed by a team of 20,000 volunteers who had put together a sensational three-day event. On the right, one could see the delegations from Taiwan, Singapore and Hong Kong, clad in red and yellow, mingling with their brethren from mainland China. In the 'green zone' sat Iraqis with green flags beside the Iranians—their mortal enemies, along with enthusiastic Israeli youth. Indeed, it was an extraordinary spectacle.

'How is this possible?' wondered a questioning mind in the third row. 'How can so many people from countries that have been at loggerheads with each other for decades, if not centuries, come together on one platform and really appear to love each other?'

Far away on the dais sat a small yet formidable bearded figure, an enigmatic smile on his face. Though expected to speak by all, Sri Sri Ravi Shankar (henceforth referred to as Sri Sri) did not utter a word. And yet, over the span of three days, nobody left dissatisfied. Swamis in orange robes, bishops in white cassocks, maulvis with their skull caps, Jain and Buddhist monks, Orthodox priests, Jewish leaders—they were all there.

On the second day, two million people sat silent, eyes closed, in the largest meditation camp ever conducted, merging their minds into one intent—world peace. On the final day, at 5.45 p.m. on a blazing Sunday evening, silence descended upon the multitude again as Sri Sri himself conducted the sudarshan kriya. Without so much as a murmur, the crowd happily settled down wherever it could and did the rigorous *kriya* to continuous chants of *so hum so hum*.

And for the first time, the man in the third row realized the power of silence.

In the end, everyone assembled, including mediapersons, stood in awe, some with tears in their eyes. Dr A.P.J. Abdul Kalam, the former President of India, summed it up best when he said, 'Sri Sri's mission of an "enlightened society" is indeed an extraordinary vision—of providing education along with a value system, religion that transforms into spirituality and economic development for social transformation.'

That was when the man in the third row decided to find out more about the man behind the enigmatic smile. How was he going to bring about this change in human consciousness, especially at a time when things looked so bleak?

Chapter One

The Art of Living

Well, *I* am that doubting journalist and my name is François Gautier. The first question I asked when I set out on this journey was: 'Who is Sri Sri?'

Today as we have entered the second decade of the second millennium, humanity is at a crossroads, neck-deep in conflicts, confrontation and war. French philosopher André Malraux had famously declared that the twenty-first century would have to come alive, spiritually, if it did not want to descend into oblivion. This means that we have about ninety years to remedy the dire state of our planet and avoid the *pralaya* that many have predicted for this age, the *Kali Yuga*.

But what would a 'spiritual' twenty-first century be like? I got my glimpse of it during those three days of celebration in Bangalore. It was wonderful to see people from diverse backgrounds, cultures, different languages and ways of being in complete harmony with each other. While waiting for Sri Sri to appear on the stage for the celebrations to begin, some people began to chant *Aum* in a corner. Meanwhile, as it was time for their evening prayers, some of the Muslims present simply put out their mats to offer *namaaz*. It was such a powerful moment that I had to pinch myself to ensure that I was not dreaming! Indeed, it was a lesson in 'unity in diversity', a baby step towards spiritualizing the twenty-first century. A century in which we would begin accepting each other; in which the children of the world would learn about the greatness of every religion, country and culture, while being grounded in the goodness of their own civilization and religion. A century in which the world's religions would acknowledge that their gods, avatars and prophets were not exclusive, and that each had come at a particular place and age to help humanity on its road to perfection. An era that would culminate in a caring, developed world in which countries would not attempt to impose their way of thinking or being upon others.

Sadly, what we see today is that, for the most part, children are still taught the supremacy of their own traditions to the exclusion of all else, and groomed in subtle and not-so-subtle ways to look down upon other traditions. Some of the major monotheist religions still believe that their gods are the only legitimate ones and continue to impose their faith upon other cultures by guile or violence, just as the West continues to coerce the so-called developing world into accepting the 'Coca Cola, McDonalds and MTV civilization' which has proved disastrous for its own civilization.

Watching the stage filled with dignitaries from all over the world and surrounded by people of all hues, I thought how wonderful it would be if the world leaders present there could take back the lessons on acceptance and assimilation to their countries and help bring about an era of true brotherhood.

How prepared then was humanity for this next stage of human evolution? How was one to live a better life? How could we love one another and understand each other better? Question after question preoccupied my mind as I walked towards the dining hall in Sri Sri's Bangalore ashram, coming to an abrupt halt as I bumped into another person. I looked up apologetically to see a kindly young man who just smiled my apology away. Walking together to the dining hall, I learnt that this young man was a taxi driver from Mumbai who had once driven a client to a yoga and pranayama *shibir* conducted by Sri Sri in Mumbai and instinctively decided to follow the orderly crowd of smiling faces into the ground, where he had caught a glimpse of Guruji, as Sri Sri is affectionately known. There was something about Sri Sri and his talk about releasing stress through pranayama exercises that made Manoj decide, 'Great! This is just what I need, for there can be no job more stressful than driving a taxi in Mumbai!' He then did the course and ultimately became a teacher as well, and now imparts his knowledge to auto and taxi drivers in Mumbai.

Without a doubt, humanity needs to be spiritualized at the base, the grassroots. It has to move from the religious to the spiritual, from narrow thinking to a global consciousness, from the exclusive to the inclusive, and from linear to circular thought, where one rises above all points of view to scale the summit where all truths become one.

And what could be the best tools to bring about that tremendous change?

- Pranayama, that ancient and exact science that teaches us how to tap the goldmine within ourselves—our own breath;
- Meditation, the crowning glory of all spiritual practices that soothes the nervous system, stills the perpetual vicious circle of thought and elevates our consciousness;
- Knowledge about ourselves and the worlds beyond our limited physical world: why life, why death, why suffering, and where are we headed.

Once upon a time, this knowledge had been a living truth—from Mesopotamia to Greece, from China to Egypt and from the Celts to the Hindus. But today it has disappeared, just as these civilizations themselves exist only in history books. One country alone still holds that secret knowledge within herself—India, which has kept this spiritual science alive and now sends it forth into the world, as Swami Vivekananda and Sri Aurobindo had prophesied long ago.

'Could the vehicle of this spiritualization of humanity be the founder of the Art of Living, Sri Sri?' I asked myself.

Who Is Sri Sri?

Before I narrate Sri Sri's official biography, let me briefly share what he has come to mean to me. Sri Aurobindo once said, 'Even if God manifests himself right in front of you, you will not recognize him.' Some who are lucky, or perhaps clairvoyant, instantly recognize Lord Krishna or Shiva or Jesus Christ in their very first meeting with Sri Sri. Not me, though. I was not looking for a god, or even a guru. I just wanted to learn pranayama to improve my breathing and energy levels. As simple as that. Secondly, although I had lived in India for several years, I harboured a certain suspicion of gurus, and wondered about this long-haired, bearded and garlanded man who showered rose petals on his ecstatic, hymn-singing disciples. But even as the mind thinks, judges and doubts, the soul that had brought me here in the first place immediately recognized the divine being in front of me. Thus, I returned again and again to him, in spite of my doubting mind, and learnt pranayama and meditation techniques to still the mind and was lead deeper into self-discovery. Over time, I recognized the divinity in his rock-solid equanimity and boundless energy. Sometimes, the full force of it exploded in front of me when I had glimpses of him in a trance, one of the occasions being the Navaratri celebrations in October-November. I discovered how indeed he was a 'guru of action'—how nothing escaped his attention, how no area of our earthly life was unworthy of his attention. From four in the morning to two at night, he was always on the move, his attention everywhere, his concern boundless, his smiling care extended to all. Truly, the guru of the Art of Living was a guru of our times, a guru of the moment, and as we shall see, a true apostle of peace.

When you ask Sri Sri who he is, he always answers, smiling, 'I am a child that never grew up.' This enigmatic personality was born on 13 May 1956 in Papanasam, Tamil Nadu, to Acharya Venkataratnam and Vishalakshi. His parents named him Shankar as he was born on the birth star of Adi Shankara, the eighth century Hindu saint. It was apparent from early on that Sri Sri was destined to lead a spiritual life. From a very young age, he would meditate and chant *slokas* from the Bhagavad Gita. As a young boy he would often tell his friends, 'People all over the world are waiting for me.'

Recognizing his spiritual bent of mind, Sri Sri's parents ensured that his education would encompass both spiritual and worldly knowledge. He completed his degree in science and Vedic literature by the age of seventeen. While growing up, he met many prominent spiritual teachers, including Maharishi Mahesh Yogi, the founder of the Transcendental Meditation Movement, with whom he spent several years in Rishikesh. His influence and spiritual research impelled the teenaged Ravi Shankar to embark on the path of asceticism.

In 1982, Sri Sri returned to Shimoga, Karnataka and went into a ten-day-long silence. He emerged from this silence with the sudarshan kriya, a powerful yet simple breathing technique that eliminates stress and energizes one physically and emotionally. Later, as he taught his first course, the people of Shimoga recognized that a great spiritual master stood before them. When asked to speak, Guruji lovingly shared his insights and his silence. Thus began his travels around the world, teaching people the art of living life simply, joyfully and effectively. The first course had five people. Sri Sri himself taught the course for the next four years. In 1986, the first teachers' training course was conducted and seven teachers were trained to take this knowledge to the world.

Today there are over 6000 teachers of the sudarshan kriya all over the world. Hundreds of thousands of people and communities across the globe have experienced physical, mental, emotional and spiritual transformation thanks to the various programmes offered by the Art of Living Foundation, which is spread over 140 countries, while the International Association for Human Values (IAHV), headquartered in Geneva, has done peace work in regions as diverse as Iraq, Kosovo and Afghanistan. Felicitated the world over by governments, Sri Sri has been instrumental in enabling people to lead happier, healthier and stress-free lives. In a world rent by conflict, Sri Sri has carried forth the eternal message of love, service and revival of human values, addressing diverse audiences such as the United Nations and the World Economic Forum, not to mention various parliaments, academic and social institutions.

Yet, beyond all these visible achievements, he is a guru with a personal touch. As he says, 'We are here to develop the individual, not a movement.' He ignites the flame of love in one heart, which in turn transforms another ten, which goes on to touch another hundred. Over two decades, he has been a role model, inspiring people from all walks of life, offering opportunities for leadership and service to every single person connected to him. Indeed, his wisdom, love, compassion and gentle wit have given a whole new dimension to spirituality.

What Is the Art of Living?

I have lived in India for over three decades and was a long-time resident of Auroville, that unique enterprise that aims at human unity with the extraordinary Matrimandir—a haven of silence and beauty—at its centre. India has given me a lot, professionally, emotionally and above all, spiritually, through my association with the Mother, whom I had the grace to meet, and Sri Aurobindo, the living inspiration behind my work.

And yet, knowing the Art of Living was like coming home. The warmth, the welcome and the dedication to *seva* never ceases to amaze me, even after so many years. Sri Sri's disciples are not only totally devoted to him but also untiring in fulfilling his wishes. Of course, all human beings have two faces, as we are taught in part I of the Art of Living course. The movement has seen its share of power struggles, ego clashes and problems.

However Sri Sri always smoothes things out—with a smile, a word or an injunction—without ever raising his voice.

Sri Sri's ashram in Bangalore is an ever-evolving abode of peace, light and learning. The meditation hall, named Vishalakshi Mantap in memory of Sri Sri's mother, is a thing of unceasing wonder and beauty. You sit there, close your eyes, let the world's clamour fade away, and feel peace, stillness and joy gently pervade you, wiping out all the tension, all the pain. This is what Art of Living means to me.

When I began writing this book, I would follow Bhanumati Narasimhan, Sri Sri's sister and his first disciple, around everywhere with my tape recorder to help her recount the origins of the Art of Living. Bhanu told me that in order to implement and coordinate the various global projects for personal development and social welfare, Sri Sri established two international institutions: the Bangalore-based Art of Living Foundation in 1982, which has since promoted self-development and fostered physical, mental, and spiritual-health related programmes worldwide; and the Geneva-based IAHV in 1997, which focusses on ways and means of revitalizing universal human values. Today both Art of Living and IAHV have been accorded special consultative status by the Economic and Social Council of the United Nations, and have permanent representatives at the United Nations in New York, Geneva and Vienna.

In India, Bhanudi said, the Art of Living courses are taught under the aegis of the Ved Vignan Mahavidyapeeth (VVM) that Sri Sri established in 1981. She recounted how it all started in a small house in Jayanagar in Bangalore, now known as Gyan Mandir, where Sri Sri started his first Vedic school. To this day, these Vedic schools provide value-based education, integrating ancient spiritual heritage with a modern scientific temper. According to Shankar Ram, a Bangalore-based clinical psychologist, studies show that students who learn the Vedas possess a better overall memory in comparison to those who attend regular schools. Gyan Mandir was where the first Art of

Living courses were taught and where Namrita and I did our Part I course at the behest of a friend. This was also where I felt the first pull towards the organization.

I have always been amazed to see how people from all walks of life come together during the Art of Living courses in total harmony and oneness, leaving behind the strife of their daily lives. I was not surprised therefore when Rajshree Patel, one of the senior-most teachers of the Art of Living, told me how this course has received acceptance from millions of people from diverse social, cultural and ethnic backgrounds today.

Bhanudi also recounted how the course fee has helped the organization establish and run Sri Sri Vidya Mandir schools that provide health care and vocational education in tribal and rural areas all over India. Bhanudi, who is closely associated with education, talked passionately about the school founded near Sri Sri's Bangalore ashram to provide holistic education to over a thousand children from nearby villages. The next day, she escorted me to this school.

The sight of smiling faces alighting from the bus to start their day at school was enough to gladden my heart. These children looked so different from my memories of schoolmates in France! Meena, a young girl of about eight, walked up to me confidently to ask my name and which country I was from, a question I am often asked in India by way of a conversation starter. I was struck by the confidence of this young child as she spontaneously recounted how she used to stay at home to take care of her younger sibling and do the housework while her parents went out to earn their daily wages. All this changed when one of the Art of Living volunteers visited her parents and encouraged them to send both their daughters to school. Initially, Meena's parents were unsure as they did not have the means to educate both children; but knowing that the school would feed the children, along with providing books, uniforms and health care, they happily consented to send Meena and her sister to school. Today, over 15,000 students in over eighteen states across India benefit from more than 100 such Sri Sri Ravi Shankar Vidya Mandir schools.

Sri Sri often says, 'The purpose of education is to increase awareness and refine our behaviour, our attitude and our ability to perceive things.' Speaking to the teachers in one of these schools was an eye opener for me. Their smiles said it all—they did not have the harried and stressed look of the teachers who had taught me all those years ago. Observing them, I realized their gentle love and care for their students and how they inculcated human values in them by setting an example by practising those values in their own lives.

At present, there are over seventy-eight urban schools and eight institutes of higher learning run by the Art of Living Foundation, including the Sri Sri Centre for Media Studies that offers competitive courses in both print and visual media. As its director Vinod Menon puts it:

> It is imperative that we train a whole new generation of Indian journalists. As you know, one of the biggest problems facing us today is that Indian journalists are not always aware of their own culture and roots and therefore tend to have a negative outlook about India, which in turn influences foreign correspondents posted here. At the Sri Sri Centre for Media Studies, we teach the best of both print and electronic journalism along with classes on Indian history, the ideals of journalism, as well as the basic course part I, so that the twin ancient Indian sciences of pranayama and meditation hone the minds of aspiring journalists.

In Indian tradition, energy or *shakti* is seen as feminine, without which nothing can be achieved. Sri Sri's words—'Women are innately powerful; they only need to realize it'—inspired his father to start Vista, a vocational centre for rural women that imparts skills such as tailoring, painting, and making incense sticks, jute bags and other artefacts. Over the past two decades, Vista has transformed the lives of thousands of women and girls in more than thirty villages in and around Bangalore. As Sri Sri puts it, 'When you train a woman, you help a family, the society and the nation.'

Sri Sri has always emphasized that the object of rural development should be to empower people and to encourage them to take responsibility and take care of their environment. As Nirali, a young volunteer from Gujarat who is closely involved with rural development work, explains:

> All volunteers involved in development work go to the villages to identify young men and women with leadership qualities. They then undergo the Youth Leadership Training programme (YLTP) which incorporates traditional techniques of yoga, meditation and pranayama, along with training in communication skills, leadership and entrepreneurship. Once their training is over, the young 'Yuvacharyas' become the agents of change in their communities.

The youth leaders initiate change through the 5H programmes that focus on health, hygiene, homes, human values and harmony in diversity. The objective of these programmes is economic and social self-reliance at the individual, community and societal level. Over 50,000 youths have been trained to implement the motto 'Yoga in Action, Adventure in Service' to become strong and effective leaders of change. The 5H programme approach has found international recognition and has now been implemented in South Africa, Poland, Kosovo, Afghanistan, Iraq, Iran, USA, South America and Indonesia, under the aegis of the IAHV.

Sri Sri has also designed a course for the youth called the Youth Empowerment Seminar (YES) since according to him the need of the hour is to channelize the abundant energy of the youth towards constructive activities. The YES course includes dynamic body exercises, breathing techniques and processes that are easy to integrate into the lives of youngsters. Participants are encouraged to care and share, to build friendships and feel one with everyone, whatever their religion, culture or background, and take up welfare projects that give back to the society.

The All Round Training in Excellence (ART Excel) course is Sri Sri's gift to children belonging to the eight to fourteen years age group. This course, which combines fun with learning, is a mixture of yoga, pranayama, activities that nurture creativity, games, music and dance, and helps children develop confidence and handle challenges and pressure in a positive manner. 'More than winning or losing, it is the fun that counts,' says a smiling Ajay from Mumbai. 'It is like an energy bar!' gushes ten-year-old Rebecca from America.

The Divya Samaj Nirman (DSN) course empowers people to contribute to a better and more peaceful society, while the APEX course is aimed at introducing spiritual values to the corporate world and includes stress management tools for functioning more effectively in an organization. Then there are the Nav Chetna Shibirs or the Breath-Water-Sound (BWS) workshops that empower slum-dwellers, factory workers and villagers. The IAHV also conducts these workshops, designed to eliminate stress. Over four million people from religions around the world have experienced its benefits. Apart from these, there are specific Art of Living courses designed for people with HIV-AIDS and cancer, as well as for people suffering from substance abuse. Studies conducted at the Navjyoti Drug Rehabilitation Centre in Delhi found that addiction levels dropped drastically after patients underwent the Art of Living course and also noted a marked change in the attitude of the patients, who became noticeably calmer, were able to control their anger better and felt light in body and mind. They also revealed that they experienced a certain sense of tranquility in their body and that their aches and pains had disappeared.

Then there are Art of Living courses designed for the police and armed forces that have done yeoman service in prisons around the world. Ajay Agarwal, director, Tihar Jail, New Delhi, says, 'The Art of Living courses have shown a positive path even to prisoners under the high-security risk category and have helped draw out their inner harmony, which is in turn reflected in their outer lives.'

While at the Bangalore ashram, I was surprised to hear cries of excitement from the direction of the amphitheatre. I could not believe my eyes when I saw a game of football being played between Iraqis and Iranians, who were in the ashram to participate in a course specially organized for Islamic nations. I gleefully joined the game and after it was over, we all walked together to the cafeteria to cool off. Farad from Iraq told me how this course had changed his life:

> I used to be sad, depressed and angry at the world. I was full of fear and could not sleep peacefully since, even in my dreams, I would see and hear bombs and cries of anguish of those injured or dying. Now, after just five days, I am able to sleep, I feel more at peace with the world, and am much happier than when I came. My life has found meaning again.

This is an oft-echoed sentiment by victims of trauma, whether in Afghanistan, Iraq, Bosnia or Serbia, as also amongst survivors of the tsunami, floods or earthquakes, as well as victims of the terrorist attacks of 9/11 or the November 2008 Mumbai terror attacks, all of whom have been touched by the care given to them by the Art of Living volunteers during their hour of need. These seva workers not only take care of victims' rehabilitation and provide food, shelter and medicines, but also cater to their emotional and psychological needs. As Sri Sri often says, 'Peace is your innate nature; it cannot go away from you.' The many programmes conducted by Art of Living help regain that innate sense of peace and balance lost through stress, illness and accidents, even as they help transform feelings of rage, hopelessness and other such negative emotions into positive energy. The aim is to bring about peace: step by step, individual by individual, country by country.

Are You Breathing Right?

Breath is the link between our body, mind and spirit. Over 90 per cent of the toxins in our body are eliminated through our breath. However, medical studies show that the average person uses only a fraction of his/her lung capacity. Since our lungs determine the amount of oxygen in our systems, not to mention the quantity and quality of toxin removal, not breathing right may be costing you a clean bill of health, among other things! Take a quick look to see if you are breathing right or if a trip to your nearest Art of Living teacher is in order.

TEST 1 – The Chest Breather

Get in Position:

1. Lie on your back.
2. Place a hand on your upper chest and another on your abdomen.

The Test:

Does the hand on your chest move when you breathe and the one on your abdomen remain static? If yes, chances are that you are a chest breather. A sign of inefficient breathing is when there is more than a slight movement of the chest while you breathe.

TEST 2 – The Shallow Breather

Get in Position:

1. Lie on your back.
2. Place your hands around your lower ribs.

The Test:

Are your ribs motionless when you breathe? Is there an easy expansion of the lower ribs when you breathe in and a gentle contraction when you breathe out? If not, then chances are that you are a shallow breather—even if your belly moves—and you are not using the full capacity of your lungs to breathe.

TEST 3 – The Over-breather

Contrary to what it sounds, over-breathing is actually counter-productive to the breathing process. A normal breathing cycle has a longer exhalation than inhalation. Reversing this process inhibits the process of removing toxins through the breath. To check if you are one, try the following test:

Get in position:

1. Lie down and relax your body for a few minutes.
2. Wait until your breathing is natural and even.

The Test:

Count the length of your exhalation and compare it to the length of the next inhalation. The exhalation should be slightly longer. If not, you are an over-breather. As a second test, try to shorten your inhalation as compared to your exhalation and see if it gives you an uncomfortable feeling.

TEST 4 – The Breath-holder

Holding one's breath after inhaling is probably the most common poor breathing habit. This is especially noticeable after exercise. To check if this is yours, pay attention to the transition from inhalation to exhalation. A breath-holder usually feels a 'catch' and may actually struggle to initiate the exhalation. Try relaxing your abdomen as you breathe out, this will help reduce the 'breath-holding'.

TEST 5 – The Reverse Breather

Reverse breathing happens when the diaphragm is pulled into the chest on breathing in and drops into the abdomen while breathing out. To determine if you are a reverse breather, try the following test:

Get in position:

1. Lie on your back.
2. Place your hands on your abdomen.

The Test:

Check if your abdomen slowly flattens as you exhale and rises gently as you inhale. If the opposite occurs, you are a reverse breather.

   If you are not (and even if you are), then you are ready for part I of the Art of Living courses.

The Art of Living courses, both part I and II, help eliminate stress from everyday life through simple breathing techniques. People turn to these courses to lower their stress levels and find renewed vigour and clarity in their lives. Along with pranayama, mediation and yoga, this course re-establishes basic human values in our consciousness through simple processes. The heart of the course is the sudarshan kriya.

Chapter Two

The Art of Healing

Today, we need not only the art of living but also the art of healing both the body and the mind. The stress and various kinds of ailments triggered by wrong ways of thinking, working and senseless competition have taken a severe toll upon our bodies. When the mind is sick, unhappy, and full of hatred, the body suffers, as a result of which, debilitating ailments thrive in it.

When you learn the Art of Living, the healing hand of the Grace is automatically placed upon you, as so many examples in this book will illustrate. Art of Living is based on the science of breath, so let us begin by looking at the importance of breath.

Breathing is important for two reasons. It is the only means to supply oxygen to the body, so vital for our survival. The second function of breathing is that it is the main means of getting rid of waste products and toxins from the body.

Why Is Oxygen So Vital?

Oxygen is the most vital source of nourishment for our body. It is essential for the functioning of the brain, nerves, glands and internal organs. We can do without food for weeks and without water for days, but not without oxygen for even a few minutes. The lack of a proper supply of oxygen would lead to the degradation of all vital organs.

The brain requires more oxygen than any other organ. If it doesn't get enough, the result is mental sluggishness, negative thoughts and depression, and eventually, a decline in vision and hearing. As we age, the oxygen supply to all parts of the body is reduced, especially so if we lead a poor lifestyle. A heart attack happens when an acute circulation blockage deprives the heart of oxygen. If this occurs to the brain, the outcome is a stroke.

Lack of oxygen is a major and proven cause of heart disease, stroke and cancer. Medical research done in Germany as far back as 1947 demonstrated that when oxygen was withdrawn, normal body cells could turn cancerous, while research conducted at Baylor University, USA, proved that you can reverse arterial disease in monkeys by infusing oxygen into the diseased arteries.

Thus, oxygen is critical to our well-being, and any effort to increase its supply to our body, and especially to the brain will only pay rich dividends. Yogis realized the vital importance of an adequate oxygen supply millions of years ago, and developed and perfected various breathing techniques. These breathing exercises are particularly important for people who have sedentary jobs. Their brains are oxygen-starved and their bodies are just 'getting-by'. They feel tired, nervous, irritable and less productive, as a result of which they sleep badly at night, leading to getting a bad start the next day and thus continuing the vicious cycle. This situation also lowers their immune system, making them susceptible to catching colds, flu and other 'bugs'.

Oxygen Purifies the Bloodstream

One of the major secrets of vitality and rejuvenation is a purified bloodstream. The quickest and most effective way to purify the bloodstream is to take in extra supplies of oxygen from the air we breathe. Oxygen removes toxins from the body in addition to recharging the body's batteries, viz. the solar plexus. In fact, most of our energy requirements come not from food but from the air we breathe. By purifying the bloodstream, every part of the body and mind is rejuvenated.

Medical Science Verifies the Importance of Oxygen

Scientists have discovered that the chemical basis of energy production in the body is a chemical called Adenosine Triphosphate (ATP). If something goes wrong with the production of ATP, it results in reduced vitality, disease and premature ageing. Scientists have also discovered that oxygen is critical to the production of ATP; in fact, it is its most vital component.

Yoga and pranayama permit us to tap into this vital nutrient. This is validated by the experience of a course participant, Marg L. Nelson from Australia:

> What can I say that won't sound insincere? At the age of sixty-four, I was suffering from a weak heart and had had a stroke. Needless to say, I had all the problems that go with these. I was sceptical what this course would do for me that my doctor had not already done. However, as the days progressed and we continued to learn and practise the breathing exercises, I found that my memory and concentration had improved, that my emotions were no longer on a roller-coaster. I slept really well (my husband told a friend that I sleep 'the sleep of the just'), had more energy. I loved what was happening to me. My well-being began to perk up from day one, while my overall health improved within days. Now I'm fitter, more confident and raring to go. After forty days of continued practice, I feel younger, don't get fatigued like I did earlier, have gained in flexibility, especially of the ankles, and am more alert than ever. My confidence has improved and I plan to go swimming this summer, something I have not been able to do for the last two decades! My doctor is very surprised, though cautious, at all these changes in my health and fitness. However, he is agreeable to review my medication if I am able to maintain my improved health for another three months.

I am pretty excited since in the past my medication has only been increased, never decreased. My transformation has definitely begun.

The Importance of Healthy Breathing

We know how to breathe since it is something that we do automatically and naturally. We breathe even when we are not quite aware of it. So it seems foolish to think that one can be taught how to breathe. Yet, one's breathing becomes modified and restricted in various ways, not just momentarily but habitually. We develop unhealthy habits without being aware of it. We tend to assume slouched positions that diminish lung capacity and take shorter breaths. We also live in conditions or adopt habits that are detrimental to the well-being of our respiratory system.

As mentioned earlier, scientists have known for long that there is a strong connection between respiration and mental states. Improper breathing leads to diminished mental ability. The converse is true as well—it is well-known that mental tension leads to restricted breathing.

A normally sedentary person, when confronted with a perplexing problem, tends to lean forward, draw his arms together and bend his head—postures that result in reduced lung capacity. The more intense the concentration, the tenser the muscles grow. The muscles in the arms, neck and chest tend to contract while the muscles that move the thorax and control inhalation and muscular tenseness clamp down and restrict exhalation. The breaths become shorter and shorter. After an extended period of intense concentration, the whole system seems to be frozen in a certain posture. Since the body almost stops breathing, we feel fatigued due to the decreased circulation of blood and the decreased availability of oxygen for the blood. As our duties, responsibilities and their attendant problems become more demanding; we develop a habit of forgetting to breathe.

What's Wrong With the Way We Breathe?

Animals which breathe slowly live the longest, the elephant being the most visible example. More often than not, our breathing is too shallow and too quick. The body needs to breathe more slowly and deeply. Quick, shallow breathing results in oxygen starvation which means that we do not take in sufficient oxygen and exhale sufficient carbon dioxide, leading to a build-up of toxins. This leads to reduced vitality, premature ageing, poor immune system and a myriad of other problems. Each cell in the body requires oxygen and our level of vitality is but a product of the health of all the cells. Shallow breathing does not exercise the lungs enough, so they lose some of their function, causing a further reduction in vitality.

Why Is Our Breath Fast and Shallow?

There are several reasons for shallow breathing. The major ones are:

- We are in a hurry most of the time, and our movements and breathing follow this pattern.
- The increased stress of modern living makes us breathe more quickly and less deeply.
- We get too emotional—too excited, too angry, too anxious—too easily. These negative emotional states affect the rate of breathing, causing it to become fast and shallow.
- Modern technology and automation have reduced our need for physical activity. We work indoors more often, which means that there is less need to breathe deeply. Over a period of time, the body adopts the shallow breathing patterns that it is used to.

As we go through life, these bad breathing habits become part of our lifestyle. Unless we do something to reverse these habits, we risk suffering permanent problems. The good news is that these habits are reversible. However, before we change them, we need to recognize and accept that there is a need for change and see the benefits of good breathing techniques for ourselves.

The Effects of Shallow Breathing

The effects of shallow breathing are:

- Reduced vitality: since oxygen is essential for the production of energy in the body.
- Lower immunity: since oxygen is essential for healthy cells, shallow breathing reduces our resistance to diseases. We catch more colds and develop other ailments more easily. Lack of sufficient oxygen reaching the cells is known to be a major contributing factor in cancer, heart disease and strokes.

With our 'normal' sedentary way of living, we only use about one tenth of our total lung capacity. This is sufficient to survive and just tick over, but not sufficient for a high vitality level, long life and high resistance to diseases.

Ancient yogis knew the importance of correct breathing and developed techniques not only to increase health and life span, but also to attain superconscious states. And that's exactly what Steve experienced after just four weeks of pranayama practice. He found that he had zero fatigue during the day and felt much fitter:

> My immunity seems to have improved, for I have not had a cold since the course! I find I am better able to deal with stress, am much happier and more relaxed. Stress just seems to bounce off, that's the only way I can describe it. I am doing the breathing exercises every day and feel fantastic every day. I feel I have discovered my essence.

The Medical Viewpoint

Modern science agrees with the ancient yogis on the subject of shallow breathing. An editorial in the *Journal of the Royal Society of Medicine* suggests that fast, shallow breathing can cause fatigue, sleep disorders, anxiety, stomach upsets, heartburn, gas, muscle cramps, dizziness, visual problems, chest pain and palpitations. Scientists have also found that a lot of people who believe they have heart disease really suffer from improper breathing.

Importance of Breathing through the Nose

The first rule for correct breathing is that we should breathe through the nose. This may seem obvious, but many people breathe principally through the mouth. Breathing through the mouth can adversely affect the development of the thyroid gland, and even arrest the mental development of children.

The nose has various defence mechanisms to prevent impurities and excessively cold air from entering the body. At the entrance to the nose, a screen of hair traps dust, tiny insects and other particles that may injure the lungs. After the entrance of the nose, there is a long, winding passage lined with mucous membranes, where excessively cool air is warmed and very fine dust particles that might have escaped the hair screen are caught. Next, in the inner nose are glands which fight off any bacilli which may have slipped through the other defences. The inner nose also contains the olfactory organ, which enables our sense of smell and also detects any poisonous gases that may injure our health. The mouth is bereft of such defence mechanisms.

Yogis believe that the olfactory organ has another function, i.e., the absorption of *prana* from the air. If you breathe through your mouth all the time, as many people do, you are cheating yourself of all this free energy and this could be a major factor in lowered resistance to disease, impairing the functioning of your vital glands and nervous system. Add to this the fact that pathogens can enter the lungs via the mouth, and it is evident that it's impossible to be healthy if you breathe through the mouth.

It is easy to break the habit of breathing through the mouth. Just keep your mouth closed and you will automatically breathe through your nose!

The Benefits of Deep Breathing

Let us now summarize the benefits of deep breathing:

- Improvement in the quality of blood due to increased oxygenation in the lungs, aiding in the elimination of toxins from the system.
- Improvement in the digestion and assimilation of food: Digestive organs receive more oxygen, and hence operate more efficiently. The digestion is further enhanced by the fact that the food is oxygenated more.
- Improvement in the health of the nervous system, including the brain, spinal cord, nerve centres and nerves: Improved oxygenation and hence nourishment of the nervous system improves the health of the whole body since the nervous system connects all parts of the body.
- Rejuvenation of the glands, especially the pituitary and pineal glands: The brain has a special affinity to oxygen, requiring three times more oxygen than does the rest of the body. This has far-reaching effects on our well-being.
- Rejuvenation of the skin: The skin becomes smoother and there is a visible reduction in facial wrinkles.
- Improvement in the health of abdominal and other organs: The movement of the diaphragm during deep breathing massages the abdominal organs such as the stomach, small intestine, liver and pancreas; and also the heart, stimulating blood circulation in all organs. The lungs become healthy and powerful, acting as a good insurance

against respiratory problems. Deep, slow yoga breathing also reduces the workload of the heart. Firstly, deep breathing leads to more efficient lungs, which means that more oxygen is brought into contact with the blood sent to the lungs by the heart. So, the heart doesn't have to work as hard to deliver oxygen to the tissues. Secondly, deep breathing leads to a greater pressure differential in the lungs, which leads to an increase in the circulation, thus resting the heart a little. The result is a more efficient, stronger heart that operates better and lasts longer. It also means reduced blood pressure and less chances of heart disease.

- Controlling weight: If you are overweight, the extra oxygen helps burn up the excess fat more efficiently. If you are underweight, the extra oxygen feeds the starving tissues and glands. In other words, yoga helps you reach the ideal weight, making you feel healthier, both physically and mentally.
- Relaxation of the mind and body: Slow, deep, rhythmic breathing causes a reflex stimulation of the parasympathetic nervous system, which results in a reduction of the heart rate and relaxation of the muscles. These two factors cause a reflex relaxation of the mind, since the mind and body are interdependent. In addition, the oxygenation of the brain normalizes brain function, reducing anxiety levels.
- Enhanced breathing capacity: Deep breathing exercises enhance the elasticity of the lungs and ribcage. This creates an increased breathing capacity all day, not just during the actual exercise period. This means that we derive the benefits of the deep breathing exercises all day.

The pranayama techniques taught as part of the Art of Living course show us the path to both breathing and living right.

Power of the Breath: Sudarshan Kriya

> In sleep we get rid of fatigue, but the deeper stresses remain in our body. Sudarshan kriya cleanses the system from within. The breath has a great secret to offer.
>
> —Sri Sri Ravi Shankar

Sudarshan kriya is perhaps the most loved technique of the Art of Living, a powerful breathing exercise that combines ancient knowledge with the rhythms of the breath, cleanses and energizes the body and mind, and brings about integration. It has a profound effect on the mind, body and spirit. It uses specific rhythms of breath to re-establish one's inner balance as it floods the cells of the body with oxygen and energy. As many course participants have reported, one's entire system seems to awaken and rejoice after the sudarshan kriya.

In order to understand the enormous health implications of the sudarshan kriya, one must first understand the relationship between the breath, the mind, emotions and the body. The kriya links the breath to the mind-body system in a specific way that rids the system of accumulated stress and toxins, releasing negative emotions and rejuvenating the body. Over two million people worldwide have enjoyed the benefits of the Art of Living course and the powerful sudarshan kriya technique.

Henrik Bjerring from Denmark, a gold medalist in ice-hockey, says, 'My training with the Art of Living breathing techniques has resulted in a much greater utilization of my potential. Now, stability and high quality characterize my performance.' Most course participants report a greater ease and joy in personal relationships. 'It has been a great healing for me, I feel very peaceful and one with everybody. A great joy fills my heart with love for all beings,' says Martine with gratitude. This is another oft-heard sentiment after the course. Another participant shared how the feeling of having received a lot, awakened in him a feeling of oneness with the world, and how he was inspired to take this knowledge to others so that they could benefit from it too.

Today scientific research has established pranayama's wide-ranging benefits, including stress elimination, heightened immunity, more efficient mental activity and overall well-being, suggesting that sudarshan kriya might even prevent many illnesses, including cancer and cardiac diseases.

'The healing breath relaxes you fully. Your life becomes more wholesome since the breathing technique enables the different facets of your personality to come together. Perform the healing breath and meditate. These practices completely transform you and kindle the love deep inside.' These words of Sri Sri that introduce the sudarshan kriya have inspired many to take the plunge into the sea of energy connected with the breath. Here are some observations made by course participants post-kriya:

'After the first kriya, every cell in my body felt renewed and I felt bathed in divine radiance.'

'I was blown away. Such intense energy! So much power! The feeling that I can do anything! So much love!'

'After the course I feel a sense of inner harmony. I've settled in my being.'

'While I was lying down after the kriya, it felt like someone was holding my hand. I felt like I was holding hands with God.'

One can go on and on with the different experiences of all those that I have met over the years of my involvement with the Art of Living. And yet the mind always searches for an explanation of the things that it does not understand!

As mentioned earlier, sudarshan kriya consists of the repetition of different patterns of breathing. There is not only a scientific basis to it (which we shall shortly explore), but also Sri Sri's grace and the grace of the Ineffable, the Incommensurable, the Infinite—that which is beyond us. Those of us who have experienced sudarshan kriya know how precise, minute, and effective it is and how the force of prana works in us at all levels. This is the miracle of the sudarshan kriya, and what participants take away with them while their transformation begins on all levels—physical, mental and spiritual.

Medical Explanation of Sudarshan Kriya

Individual peace, peace in society, collective peace ...
Starts from where we are ...
Within each one of us we can create that peace.

—Sri Sri Ravi Shankar

It has already been established by science that there is a direct link between the body and mind. This implies that our emotional state and thought processes affect not only the brain but also other systems, specifically the endocrine system—the hormones, and the immune system that protects us from a variety of diseases. Each of us has experienced the effect of stressful situations and a panicky state on the mind and the body. When the mind perceives fear, real or imaginary, the pulse beats faster, the heart starts pounding, one starts sweating and the skin feels cold and clammy. This happens because of the release of chemicals and hormones, including cortisol and adrenaline from the endocrine glands, and white blood cells that deal with immunity. The body is highly adaptable and can easily tackle a few stressful situations. However, when the stress becomes chronic, physiological changes become irreversible and we become susceptible to diseases such as high blood pressure, asthma, diabetes, etc. Many relaxation techniques have been developed and used to alter our reaction to stress.

Today, science is ready to go beyond the body-mind connection to the consciousness, the very source of our emotions, thoughts and physiology. Stresses are perceived only when consciousness flows outwards, when the senses, mind and emotions are connected to the outside world and environment. However, when the consciousness turns inwards, and when senses, thoughts and emotions harmonize with the consciousness (a state of 'pure' consciousness), then stresses are not perceived—irrespective of our surroundings. One has to realize and experience this state, and only then can it bring about changes in our psyche, thought processes, emotions and the body. The obvious question then would be: How can one experience this state? That is where pranayama and sudarshan kriya come in.

Before briefly dealing with the neurobiology of pranayama, it will be helpful to dwell on the meaning and significance of the word itself for a moment. Pranayama literally means 'the ebb and flow of prana or energy'. It perhaps represents a comprehensive concept of an energizing-integrating current that weaves life out of nature. It is there in the air currents of our breath, as also in the flux of bio-electricity through the myriad of axons and dendrites of the billions of nerve cells that energize and integrate our being. It is there in the energies of tens of thousands of equilibrated bio-chemical reactions integrated within and across cell barriers, tissues and organ systems to engender the marvellous phenomenon called 'life'. The word 'pranayama' thus represents the ebb and flow of this life-giving energy.

While oxygen intake and carbon dioxide expulsion are central to the process of breathing, it is important to realize that there are other equally vital neurobiological dimensions to that process—the rhythmic respiratory drive that originates in the cardio-respiratory centre of the brain stem reticular formation. There is now scientific recognition that the brain stem reticular formation and the chemo-electrical influences that emanate upward from it impinge on all the important cortical and sub-cortical neural structures that, in concert, structure 'human consciousness'. We know today that focussing conscious awareness on any bodily activity enhances blood supply and metabolic activity in the corresponding part of the brain that represents or controls that activity. Based on this fact, it can be deduced that rhythmic breathing and its variants, as prescribed in various pranayama practices, with fully focussed awareness of the process, cannot but neurobiologically influence the brain stem reticular formation and related brain activity gestalt involved in the elaboration of the human consciousness. We also know now the elaborate ways in which the influence of the mind-brain reticular formation impinges on all key ingredients of the human consciousness. In the light of these insights on the neurobiological correlates of breathing and its linkages with the neural substrate of human consciousness, it is easy to understand how pranayamic practices are key elements in yoga practices of spiritual sadhana which are prescribed for the natural expansion of human consciousness.

Over the years, as the general health and well-being started to improve in the ever growing numbers of people practising these techniques, the scientist fraternity got into the act to see how it worked. Today, scientific research is being conducted by Vinod Kochupillai, head of Medical Oncology at the All India Institute of Medical Sciences (AIIMS), New Delhi and the National Institute for Mental Health and Neurological Sciences (NIMHANS), Bangalore, on the benefits of sudarshan kriya. International symposiums have been conducted on the healing that Art of Living practitioners have experienced from a wide range of conditions such as depression, asthma, diabetes, blood pressure and cancer.

During the first international symposium on sudarshan kriya at AIIMS, New Delhi, Dr Satyan N. Das, associated professor of Biotechnology, demonstrated changes in immune parameters: how natural killer cells were significantly higher amongst regular practitioners of sudarshan kriya as compared to those who had been treated for cancer. Neurologist Dr Manveer Bhatia has conducted research on enhanced alpha, beta and theta activity in the brain which has revealed significant reduction in levels of blood lactate and enhanced antioxidant defence by practitioners of sudarshan kriya. Research done by Dr Geetha at Bangalore Medical College has shown a fall in serum cholesterol and low density lipoprotein and that there is a possibility that regular practice of sudarshan kriya might prevent heart disease. Extensive research at NIMHANS, Bangalore, has documented the benefits of sudarshan kriya in treating depressive states. If the intent of the Art of Living can be defined, it is to revive human values. The application of this precious knowledge (that sudarshan kriya helps in restoring a person's well-being) has the potential to improve the well-being of the individual, the family, the community and may even further the cause of global peace.

What Is a Miracle?

Ever heard of Descartes? René Descartes was born on 31 March 1596, in La Haye (now Descartes), Touraine, France. After studying the classics, logic and traditional Aristotelian philosophy, he came to the conclusion that the only subject which he found satisfactory was mathematics. This idea became the foundation for his way of thinking, and was to form the basis for all his works. He wrote, in 1637, a treatise on science under the title *Discours de la Methode* (The Discourse of the Method), where he came up with the famous precept: 'cogito ergo sum' or 'I think, therefore I am'. This statement became the foundation stone for later philosophical movements such as Rationalism, which emphasizes reason as a source of knowledge itself. Although many of his mathematical theories have been proven wrong today, Descartes has had a profound influence on European thinking, particularly in France. Yet, there cannot be more of an untruth than the precept 'I think, therefore I am'. Indian philosophy has known for ages that Man is not the thinking man but rather the Consciousness or *Sat-chit-ananda*. Sadly, today Descartes still rules the western thinking world. Man thinks that his mind is all, that he understands everything. Man wants to explain everything using his mind. He in his arrogance even thinks that he is responsible for all the ills that befall him, such as global warming. But there must have been other instances of global warming in the long and chequered history of our planet that had nothing to do with pollution, but occurred due to nature's apparently huge whimsical change of mood.

How then can the mind explain the divine? It is too far away from it. The questioning minds of many people will be satisfied with the scientific explanation of the sudarshan kriya.

The way I see it, life is a miracle; our breath and the way it works is a miracle. The fact that this one man, Sri Sri Ravi Shankar, has inspired thousands of volunteers to go into countries like Sudan, Iraq, Bosnia and Afghanistan to bring trauma relief to those against whom even their kith and kin had turned their backs is nothing short of a miracle!

Take the case of thirty-two-year-old Rafi Hossain, a journalist and TV anchor from Dhaka, Bangladesh. A few years ago, faced with the trauma of a broken relationship, Rafi turned to reiki, a holistic hands-on healing system. He is all praises for his reiki teacher, Ameena Ahmed, not only because she taught him how to heal himself and his friends, but also because she introduced him to the Art of Living. Rafi helped Ameena organize an Art of Living part I course in Dhaka. 'Forty-five people participated in this course,' remembers Rafi. 'Shortly after the course started, an amazing thing happened. The teacher, Partho Banerjee from Calcutta, whom I had never met before, came up to me, hugged me and said, "You will be the first Art of Living teacher from Bangladesh." I was completely taken aback and wondered what he meant by that.'

At the very first sudarshan kriya, Rafi had a strong sense of a person lingering around him. 'Someone whose clothes kept brushing against me,' Rafi adds. 'After a while this person would come up to me and say, "You'll come out of your problems." I felt completely overwhelmed.' At the sharing of experiences, Rafi asked his teacher, Partho, 'Why were you walking around me so much?' Partho replied that he had not walked at all but had been sitting quietly keeping a watch on the proceedings! Rafi was bewildered.

He found the course so helpful that at the end of the same month, February 2001, he joined his reiki teacher, Ameena, and her sister for the advanced course being held in Rishikesh, India, by the Art of Living.

'*Kahan gaye the tum* (Where were you)?' Sri Sri lovingly asked Rafi, as if he were meeting a long-lost devotee. Rafi was completely confused since he had never met Sri Sri. Nevertheless, the meeting with Sri Sri and the advanced course inspired Rafi to stay on in India. About two or three months later, he participated in the DSN (Divya Samaj Nirman) course and followed it up with his teacher's training course part I (TTC I) in 2002, where he had the opportunity to meet Guruji once again. 'He met me with such love,' says Rafi and adds that he was invited for the second part of his teacher's training course (TTC II) several times and was only able to make it in April 2005. 'You won't believe the first thing that Bharat Bhai (the TTC II teacher), whom I had never met before, said to me when he saw me,' says Rafi.

I ventured an answer, half as a joke: '*Kahan gaye the tum?*'

'Cent per cent right!' said a smiling Rafi.

My doubting mind came to the fore again, but I kept quiet.

A few days later, at the *satsang* held in the Vishalakshi Mantap, I witnessed Sri Sri Ravi Shankar calling Rafi up on the stage. 'Meet our very first Art of Living teacher in Bangladesh,' said Sri Sri, introducing Rafi to a wildly cheering audience. I could not help smiling.

What is it that makes miracles? What is that little extra element which rides on top of the medical phenomenon, or rather uses the medical phenomenon to produce a miracle? Man likes to think that miracles are haphazard, inexplicable and mysterious phenomena. 'But God,' writes Sri Aurobindo, 'works all his miracles by an evolution of secret possibilities which have been long prepared, at least in their elements, and in the end by a rapid bringing of all to a head, a throwing together of the elements so that in their fusion they produce a new form and name of things and reveal a new spirit. Often the decisive turn is preceded by an apparent emphasizing and raising to their extreme of things which seem the very denial, the most uncompromising opposite of the new principle and the new creation.'

Are miracles then only a rearranging of forces, a harmonizing of elements that have gone discordant?

 Chapter Three

Healing the Body

Ayurveda

The ancient seers of India knew that diseases of the body are often brought on by diseases of the mind. This is how, I am told, Ayurveda, the holistic science of healing was born. The idea that health is organic in character was developed in India in ancient times. The Vedas speak of the organic and holistic harmony of the spirit and body as the condition of true health. The aspiration to live a long and full life of a hundred years in perfect health was a cornerstone of the Vedic endeavour. In a hymn in the *Yajurveda*, the seeker prays for spiritual well-being supported by the physical body and nourished by contentment of all the organs and limbs, enabling the body to be stable for the entire span of life. The secrets of longevity and perfect health were known to the Vedic seers and these constituted an important part of their quest for immortality. The capacity of the body to bear the pressure of the universality of consciousness was considered to be an indispensable element in the Vedic ideal of perfection. It is for this reason that the ancient Indian system of medicine was called Ayurveda or 'The Science of Life', and the concept of physical, mental and spiritual equilibrium was its first principle.

The Ayurvedic concept of health is thus organic and holistic, and lays a special emphasis on happiness that transcends worldly happiness. Its system uses herbs, diet, lifestyle, yoga, Vedic astrology, colour therapy, energy points (using pressure, puncture, heat and oils), aromatherapy, gemstones, vastu shastra (similar to Feng Shui), and various other therapeutic means to promote 'sukham' or well-being.

'The unique constitutions of our body, mind and senses, and their complex inter-relationships with which we are born, move out of balance by inappropriate diet and lifestyles, as well as unresolved emotions,' says Sri Sri. 'These imbalances eventually manifest themselves as illnesses. Ayurvedic medicine recognizes and treats a traditional seven-stage pathogenesis, only the last two stages of which, disease and deformity, are usually diagnosed and treated in western medicine.'

Meru chikitsa is an ancient healing technique, now revived and re-introduced by Sri Sri. It endeavours to free the spine from tension that builds up in the cervical and sacral regions. It works on the four spinal sub-systems, bringing them together in harmony and releasing the tension of the spine. It is unique in the sense that it does not act on the disease as a quick-fix solution, but enables the person to heal himself in the most natural way. These methods have stood the test of time and are safe, natural and effective. This therapy aims not just at curing a disease, but also healing the person as a whole, both physically and emotionally. It works on the normal physiology rather than the diseased part of the body and empowers the body and mind to heal itself. Phenomenal results have been observed on patients with conditions such common cold, slipped disk, migraine, asthma, epilepsy and even cancer.

The traditionally built Sri Sri Ayurvedic Treatment Centre, Bangalore, set in the middle of lush coconut groves, is a haven of peace and beauty. It is also a place which has helped many a body to heal. As I waited for my appointment with Dr Neena, one of the physicians, I chatted with Suresh Kini, a chartered accountant who had been suffering from severe neck pain and headache for many years. Recalling his experiences, he said:

> The pain used to be so severe that I would even skip work. I tried different types of medicines and was also

practising yoga to get some reprieve from the pain. But nothing worked. During my advanced course here some time ago, I decided to go through the meru chikitsa sessions. Now I am so comfortable that I can travel by bus for nearly 300 kms without feeling any pain or discomfort. Also, amazingly, I'm not taking any painkillers! I enjoy a good quality of life without medicines now. Earlier I used to go for meru chikitsa as a treatment, for relief from pain. But now I take the sessions as a luxury!

Well, now it was my turn to see the doctor. I had back pain as well, due to the sedentary nature of my work for the last twenty years, as well as my constant travelling. I wanted to see if I could get some relief through ayurvedic massages. Dr Neena looked up from the letter in her hand as I walked in. I was still muttering under my breath about the state of the roads in India and wondering if it was any use to go through this treatment as it would be back to square one in a couple of days. The doctor laughed and showed me the letter in her hand. It was from Aadesh Goyal, a software engineer who was being treated for lower back pain caused by a slipped disc.

Dear Dr Neena,

How are you? I have been wanting to share with you my experience with meru chikitsa, and I thought today is a good day to reflect and send this to you.

As you know, I first suffered from a prolapsed disc in the lumbar region in early 1991, and since then it had troubled me now and then. I had problems in the cervical region as well. When the problem recurred, it usually lasted for many weeks. I had undergone both allopathic and homeopathic treatment for the same and gone through traction at least thrice.

As you know, I started on my treatment thrice a week and 'cranio' (cranial massage) once a week and it worked like magic! Within three sessions, a large portion of my pain and discomfort was gone. I was able to resume working full days, and they were hectic too, since I had been away from work for three to four weeks. I was feeling so 'normal' and good that I asked you if I could travel to Rishikesh to celebrate Diwali with Guruji in November. This, as you know, is about 275 kms from Gurgaon where I live. You said that I could. I went there, and the journey was uneventful: no pain at all! And I was able to see Guruji almost as soon as I reached there. And you know what? He punched me lightly on my cheek and asked me, 'How is your back pain now?' I was overwhelmed by his compassion.

The other thing I noticed was something uncanny. The work situations which could have in the past made me frustrated and angry were no longer successful in doing so. Speaking with you about this, you mentioned that this treatment does help in making one more peaceful. This whole therapy not only helped me with my back problem but also made me more peaceful and relaxed, more focussed on the job at hand, and hence more productive.

Though I was feeling normal, I continued the treatment for over two months on the advice of my doctors and also resumed exercise. Since then, I have felt good. The problem has not troubled me and I continue to feel peaceful and relaxed.

Now, whenever I meet anyone with a similar problem, I recommend the meru chikitsa to them. It is very easy and gentle. I must add that the doctors at your centre are compassionate and have genuine concern for patients and one instantly feels relaxed during and after the treatment, in addition to feeling better in the long-term.

Thank you for the wonderful seva you have done for me and for many others like me.

Warm regards,
Aadesh

Well, you guessed right. I underwent the treatment and my back seems to be holding up to the combined stress and strain of computers and travel!

There are moments in which all of us experience the harmony of the event we call life. These are transcendent or 'peak' experiences in which we may forget not only our self-as-object but also the world-as-object, becoming one with the experience. These are moments of sublime awareness.

These are also times of health, in the sense that they are experiences of perfect harmony. Yet, these moments invariably change and, as they do, they draw us back to the non-harmonious events that follow. We attach the term 'disease' to these disrupting events.

Health is the basic quality that a body must have and, in any given society, there is a natural recognition given to the importance of health. Health merits our keen and sustained attention since without a healthy body the potentialities of our life cannot be fully developed. The key to good health is awareness. One must know when this harmonious state of equilibrium is disturbed and there are signs of fatigue or deterioration. One must remain vigilant and immediately put things in order.

This is where our breath comes in. We have all noticed how the pattern of our breath changes when we are not well. Working with the breath makes one more intuitive regarding the body and its workings. It helps one gain personal knowledge and experience to know one's body, its usual tendencies, its weaknesses and strengths, and specific methods to bring it back into balance. One must feel responsible for one's own health. Personal responsibility for one's body is what should count more and more since this is what would bring real solutions to the problems of health management, rather than more medicines, more hospitals, and doctors.

Ayurveda and Healing

Life has four characteristics: it exists, evolves, expresses and extinguishes. And for it to exist, evolve, express and extinguish, it depends on five elements: the earth, water, air, ether and fire. According to Ayurveda, life is not a series of rigid compartments, but a harmonious flow. Even these five elements, of which the whole universe is made up of, are not tight compartments of defined objects—they flow, one into another. Each of the elements contains the other four. So, Ayurveda's approach towards life is holistic, that is, it takes into account the sum total. The most ethereal element in us is space, which the mind is made up of, and the basest is the earth element, which our bones and marrows, the structure and skin are made up of. This space is further divided into three *doshas*: *vata*, *pitta* and *kapha*, or ways of understanding the physiology, its characteristics and its effect on the mind.

When an illness arises, it occurs first in the mind and then manifests itself in the body. Simple symptoms arise, in the fluid form, which can be eradicated, and then the disease manifests itself in the most gross form, the body, where it needs medication. You might be aware of colour therapy and aromatherapy. In aromatherapy, an illness can be cured using the power of smell. It is mostly focussed on the preventive aspect. An illness can be arrested even before it rears its head. This can be achieved using fragrance, through smell, through one's breath.

The holistic approach of Ayurveda includes exercise, breathing and meditation. It is very interesting to notice the relationship between breath and the different doshas in the body, namely vata, pitta and kapha. These three doshas affect certain parts of the body more than others. For example, vata dosha is predominant in the lower part of the torso, around the stomach, intestine, etc. Diseases like gastric problems and joint aches are caused due to vata imbalance. Kapha dosha is predominant in the middle part of the torso. Cough is mainly a result of kapha imbalance.

(Perhaps the word 'cough' has been derived from the Sanskrit word 'kapha'.) And pitta affects the upper part of the body, i.e., the head. For instance, shortness of temper is a sign of pitta. So, vata, kapha and pitta are dominant in three different areas of the body.

In yoga, or in the breathing techniques, the three-stage pranayama has an effect on these three doshas. Among pranayama and other breathing techniques, there are specific breathing exercises for the lower, middle and the upper parts of the body. If you have done the three-stage pranayama, you might have noticed that after doing the pranayama you feel that the doshas in your body have altered. Something in the body has changed; you don't feel the same, you feel different, more balanced. It is pranayama that brings that balance in the system.

We have seen that the three doshas are connected with specific parts of the body. Definite rhythms or ways of breathing correct these doshas and bring balance to the respective areas. In the same way, we can find the three doshas and our nerve endings in our fingers. For example, the index finger is kapha, the middle finger is vata, and the ring finger, pitta. When you see someone's fingers, the way the fingers are formed, you can see the doshas running in the body. Practice of mudra pranayama, i.e., gently pressing the nerve endings in the fingertips and breathing with the *ujjayi* breath, also balances the doshas in the body.

How can one bring good health to one's system? First, by attending to the ether or the mind element. The first remedy is calming down the mind, coming from the most sublime aspect of creation, ether. And then the air element, the breathing, of which aromatherapy is also a part. Then light, of which colour therapy is a part. Before an illness manifests itself in the body, you can see it in the aura of a person. The technique of aura photography has gained popularity now. Some physicians have done research on this technique, especially on ulcers, cancer, and diabetes, for which ailments they have taken aura photographs and found spots even six months before they appeared as illnesses in the body. What yoga does is to energize our system with the prana, life energy or breath, thus clearing the aura and preventing the illness beforehand. The purpose of yoga is to stop the sorrow before it arises, to burn the seed of the ailment before it sprouts.

And then comes the water element. Fasting with water can bring about a lot of balance in the system. The final recourse, of course, is different herbs, medicines and surgery. All this comes in the final stage, when all else fails or when we neglect these other steps. Our breath has a lot of secrets to offer to us, because for every emotion in the mind, there is a corresponding rhythm in the breath, and each rhythm affects certain parts of the body physically. You only need to observe it to begin feeling it. The great correlation between sensations and the body, and the moods of the mind is meditation, attending to this, learning this, is meditation.

Have you observed the sensation you experience when you feel happy? You feel a sense of expansion. And if you have observed when you are miserable, it is a sensation of contraction. You feel uptight, which means that somewhere you feel tight, tense inside; there is contraction, the consciousness is contracting, that's misery, sorrow. Knowledge is knowing that which expands, this 'something' in the body that expands and contracts, feels happy and miserable, evolves and moves through the events. This knowledge, this enquiry is the study of consciousness, of life, of prana, of Ayurveda.

Yoga is something that everyone has done as a child. Have you seen a six-month-old lying on its back with its legs up? It kicks its legs and head up as well, much like the abdominal exercises that we do. And then the child assumes the cobra posture, the second posture in yogasana. Another posture is when a child bends down and turns and looks in the triangle posture, lifting one hand and placing the other one on the ground. And if you observe a sleeping child, its hands automatically form different *mudras* that correspond to its growth at that point. Children all over the world, whether in Africa, Australia, America or Asia, do the same thing. For these are the things that coordinate the body, mind and breath.

When you experience pleasure, your breath is more on the tip of the nose. This is because the sense of smell and pleasure are closely connected. Taste, smell and sex are linked. Any pleasure, and the experience of it, is associated with the rhythm of the breath which is more at the tip of the nose. And any experience of pain is associated with the root of the nose. There are many points in the body which correspond to different sensations but these are merely reflections of something which is beyond all this. What is that something? The source of life.

We can help our body heal by providing it the right nutrition, which in turn affects our mind. Food is an important source of energy. However, the wrong type of food, like stale or canned food, could create *tamas* (inertia) in the body which in turn leads to dullness of the mind. Certain types of food create *rajas* (activity or restlessness) in the body and others such as *satvik* food help focus the mind.

Kaushani, an ayurvedic practitioner who has a wealth of knowledge about diet and nutrition, explained a little about the Ayurvedic system of nutrition. Besides *ras* or taste, food has 22 pairs of *gunas* or properties that affect body temperature. These gunas are either heat-producing (*ushna*) or cooling (*shita*). Many of these properties, such as lightness versus heaviness and oiliness versus dryness, are in line with our common sense and do not come as a surprise, as we have all experienced how our bodies feel after a big, oily meal!

Suresh, who has just finished taking part in a nutrition course organized in the ashram by Kaushani, was totally enthused:

> This was a mind-boggling course. It has given me in-depth insight into the chemistry of food and has opened many avenues in my diet, which is oil-free since I have a cholesterol problem. This is a life-changing course and I

recommend it to all who wish to change their lifestyle for better health, mind and life. It is a very practical course that would help you shift from *rajasik* to satvik food.

Ayurveda and Food

There is an ongoing debate regarding the benefits of a vegetarian diet versus a non-vegetarian one. Of course, there is no one 'correct' way since food habits depend on where you live and the needs of your body in relation to your environment. However I would like to present a few facts. Science has shown that neither the human digestive tract nor the liver is designed to eliminate the uric acid that is produced from the consumption of meat. Fruits are digested in an hour, while starch and proteins require three and four hours respectively. However, meat protein takes up to seventy-two hours to be digested. Meat takes a long time to pass through our digestive tract, which is actually designed only for the consumption of fruits and grains. This means that it ferments and rots while waiting to be digested, producing toxins which lead to diseases.

Today, doctors admit that a majority of cancers and digestive problems of people are in fact the outcome of a particular lifestyle, not to mention the pesticides that the body absorbs along with its food intake. In man's rush for progress and wealth creation, many of the traditional farming methods were forsaken in order to produce more, faster. There was the much talked-about Green Revolution which saw an increased use of harmful pesticides and fertilizers in order to grow crops in abundance. These harmful products are now manifesting themselves in our bodies as different diseases. The world today is becoming more conscious of the, often poisonous, chemicals that are sprayed on crops that are used to feed both animals and humans.

In this sphere, an Art of Living initiative was taken in response to the increasing farmer suicides in India due to growing debts and economic uncertainties. The key objectives of this programme are to provide guidance to farmers to become self-reliant and build their inner confidence, to promote and revive organic farming and to educate farmers on water management and irrigation. It educates farmers on the use of quality agricultural inputs and implements aimed at higher quality yield, among others.

In 2003, Art of Living launched the Sri Sri Mobile Agricultural Institute (SSMAI) to widen its reach. SSMAI, ever since it was founded, has been bringing information and knowledge related to agriculture, right up to farmers' doorsteps, providing guidance on natural, effective practices, besides instilling self-confidence in them. This organization promotes chemical-free farming and creates awareness amidst farmers, particularly on issues concerning biodiversity, biosafety, the hazards of genetic engineering and the health risks of using chemical products. Rishi Krishi, an ancient Vedic method of organic farming, has been revived in order to conserve the environment and ensure the optimum utilization of natural resources, including rainwater harvesting.

One of the focus areas of the SSMAI is the extensive training of village youth leaders in the theoretical and practical aspects of organic farming, including participatory rural appraisal, soil and water conservation, use of agricultural implements, agricultural and horticultural crop production, dairy development, preparation of vermicompost, bio-fertilizers, bio-pesticides, value addition and post-harvest technologies. The youth are thus provided with ample experience in the practical application of whatever knowledge they acquire.

Not only does Art of Living create awareness amidst the rural community on the issue of water scarcity, it also teaches them the means by which they may overcome this problem, via rainwater harvesting and other natural water management methods. The permeation of rainwater at the field level is improved by encouraging farmers to construct counter-bunds and ponds instead of digging bore wells. Surface structures such as check dams, gabion dams and earthen dams are promoted for rainwater storage as these structures also aid the recharging of groundwater levels locally.

As I talk about this, another aspect of the master healer is brought to my notice. His attention, care and action for bringing peace to this planet are everywhere, not only in healing the body but also in healing the Earth—our mother, life giver and sustainer.

In the times that we are living in, just trying to keep up with the routine is a source of great stress. We spend hours on the computer, a few more hours stuck in traffic, eat badly and are always on the run. When I was on a lecture tour in America, I don't remember eating sitting down at a table more than four times in the three weeks that we were there. Eating breakfast—picked up from Dunkin Donuts or its kind—in the car, having a sandwich for lunch while walking to the next appointment and nourishing myself at night with yet another meal picked up at a fast-food outlet somewhere on the way back! My body did pay a price for this abuse! And people all over the world inflict this on themselves day in and day out; of course the body protests and we fall ill. Heart attacks are on the rise and an increasing number of deaths today are caused due to the unhealthy lifestyles led by the people of our age.

The Body

Education is an essential element of good health. How is it that so many years are spent in schooling and yet we have only a hazy notion of how our body functions? How is it possible that the most caring parent does not think it important for the child to have a minimum knowledge of his own body? The Youth Empowerment Seminar (YES) course is an attempt to do just this—to educate and inspire teenagers to know and take responsibility for their bodies, mind and spirit. They leave this fun-filled workshop empowered to gain health and happiness.

The youth of today are exposed to a lot more experiences than when I was growing up in France. The stresses and strains that they face are more intense. Hence, their methods to find outlets for these tensions are sometimes extreme as well, often leading them to abuse their bodies with cigarettes, drugs and alcohol. These are things that start off as being 'cool' and slowly start making addicts out of their victims. Most youngsters don't want to give up their cigarettes or their drink—at least not at that stage. However, many youngsters, once they did the YES, found something else to fill their lives and these habits just dropped.

There was a YES course just coming to an end and Bawa and Dinesh, the coordinators of that programme, invited me to come in at the session where the participants were sharing their experiences. What energy there was in the hall when I walked in! The youngsters were bubbling with enthusiasm and happiness. There was singing and dancing, laughter and tears of gratitude for all the love received and given during the last few days. This is some of the sharing that took place that day in that room charged with enthusiasm and hope for the future:

Zuhed Jamal, a student of architecture from Pakistan said:

> I had a wonderful experience at the workshop. I learnt how to breathe, concentrate and got to meet really nice people. Also, I am a very lazy person. This course helped me become active. If it were not for the course, I would have headed towards an early death due to my unhealthy habits.

Ugonma Fontaine from the USA averred:

> I feel that this workshop is a necessity in the times that we live in, especially as a Boston College student with so much going on ... school, relationships and other things. Life keeps going but we all need something to ground us.

Osama Tahir, who was taking the course for the second time, told the group:

This is a process which I despised initially, but I've learnt that daily practice helped me both physically and mentally; it helped me take control of my life, making it truly worth living. So guys, keep at it!

Then Maryam got up to share her story of addiction and how, over time, the breathing techniques helped her:

I had been dependent on drugs for a while. I never thought I had the stamina to live without them. Amazingly, I am calmer and happier. The changes have been so subtle; it's difficult to describe them. I have discovered a new energy in myself.

Malika got up next and said:

I have seen yoga on TV and read about it in books, but never learnt it for real. After joining Art of Living, I got to know the real meaning of yoga. I learnt a lot from this one week programme, and now I am capable of changing 'the world of *impossibles* to *possibles*'. The Art of Living has dared me to begin a new life.

At this, all those present cheered with great gusto and vowed, with all the enthusiasm and passion of youth, to make this world a better place.

This got me thinking that perhaps healing is more an art than a science. As in art, the mastery of technique is important but the essence of healing transcends technique or scientific knowledge. Each person is different in their make-up, physically and psychologically, hence the cure too has to be different for each individual. A true healer is one who knows intuitively both the medicine and the method appropriate to the case, to evoke the self-healing powers of the body. Sri Sri, by his very presence, is able to instil the confidence in the patient that he or she can indeed recover—even when the outcome is not certain.

Healing

Cancer

Cancer has become the plague of our times. This dreadful disease ravages the whole body, while depression and fear of death destroy the mind. However, many of the testimonies of the Art of Living practitioners show an increased sense of physical well-being and strength of mind and spirit that come from the daily practice of the kriya.

Uma has an astonishing story to tell about her cure from cancer:

> I always thought I was healthy, until January 1998 when, by accident, I discovered a lump in my right breast. I went for a general check-up in an endocrinal department, had a mammogram and FNAC, and lumps were found on both the breasts as well as in my armpits. It was an advanced stage of cancer. I was admitted into the Sanjay Gandhi Post Graduate Institute of Medical Sciences hospital in Lucknow and operated upon on 27 January 1998.
>
> After a month, I had to go for 32 sittings of radiation, followed by brachytherapy once a week on alternate breasts. After a gap of one-and-a-half months, I underwent another twelve rounds of chemotherapy (24 sittings). You have no idea what these radiation therapies do to the body and the mind ... I was put on two tablets of Temoxifin (10 mg) a day from November 1998 to November 2003 and went for check-ups every three months, which included bone scan, liver scan, mammogram and chest x-rays.
>
> Initially, the reports were not too satisfactory and everything looked pretty bleak. Then, I did my first basic course in February 1999 with Shri Yogadhi and began practising my sudarshan kriya diligently. From

that time on, my reports started showing improvement! In 2001, I went to Rishikesh for Maha Shivratri and did my second advanced course in the presence of Guruji. As luck would have it, I got to spend a good half hour with him, and when I mentioned my health problems, he said: '*Tumhe* cancer *hai? Samjho nahin hai!*' (You have cancer? Consider you don't!)

On my way back from Rishikesh, I went to Lucknow for yet another check-up. To my utter amazement, all my reports were normal, and have remained so till date! I am now off all medication. The doctors were surprised at my complete recovery and admitted that only a miracle could have brought this about! I must add that throughout my illness, there was no loss of hair and hardly any side effects. Today, I feel very grateful to Guruji, because it is only because of him that I have overcome cancer!

A real healer is truly an artist. As Catherine Coombes from New Zealand says:

I now have a sense of the moment and am able to distinguish each thought as it occurs and be aware of the result. I am even able to catch myself snoring and stop. The breathing has helped my back pain too. I feel deeply energized by the meditation. My mood swings are now almost non-existent. I was able to heal from my bowel cancer operation extremely quickly, not requiring any chemotherapy or further medical help.

Sunita Gianchandani from Mumbai talks about the same kind of experience:

I went with a very open mind and a positive attitude to the Art of Living course. Needless to say, I enjoyed it very much. The discussions and experiences of other participants made it very interesting. Learning and doing the sudarshan kriya was a wonderful experience. I can't really explain what I felt when I did it. During the course, while doing kriya, I could smell a wonderful fragrance of fresh flowers, as if someone was passing us by and showering us with these flowers.

Sometime last year I noticed that I was inexplicably putting on a lot of weight. I did not take it seriously, thinking it was just lack of exercise. After a few months, I felt that something was wrong inside me, but couldn't explain what it was. On two occasions, at my workplace, I suddenly experienced a very strange pain in my stomach. It was an unbearable shooting pain, as if something was piercing through my abdomen. I would become pale and gasp for breath. I mentioned this to a friend of mine who is a doctor. When she inspected my stomach, she felt a swelling and got worried. She asked me to get a sonogram done immediately. The sonogram report showed that a huge fibroid, the size of a coconut, had grown in my uterus. This was the cause of the unbearable pain. The report also showed a mass visible within my ovaries, which was not clearly identifiable. I was asked to see a gynaecologist immediately. At that visit, the gynaecologist told me that I would have to undergo a surgery to remove the fibroid. But before that I had to undergo some tests so that he could know what exactly the mass in the ovaries was. When my reports came, I returned to the gynaecologist. I saw the expression on his face change as soon as he saw the reports and immediately knew that something was wrong. He very honestly told me that my blood report and MRI scan reports were not a happy picture. He then said that I would have to be admitted for a major surgery immediately! I paled. I did not expect this but the look on his face told me that we did not have time. Suddenly, I became scared. All sorts of fearful thoughts came rushing to my mind.

I was to be admitted to the hospital a couple of days later. Since the time I had visited the doctor last, I had become very, very tense. Fear was writ large on my face. I prayed endlessly. While I was waiting to leave for the hospital, I switched on the TV just to divert my mind from my thoughts. Guess what I saw—Guruji, smiling at me! My fears simply vanished on seeing him and I felt very happy. I folded my hands, bowed my head in reverence, and said, 'Guruji, I am very happy to see you. I place all my fears and my health at your feet. I know you are with me and that you will take care of me.'

I had surgery the next day. I prayed endlessly on the night before the surgery. Honestly, I thought I would not come out alive. I kept thinking of Guruji. After the surgery, I was unconscious for a few days. I became very weak and lost a lot of weight.

A few days later, I received a report of the surgery. My doctor talked to my family and then I was given the shocking news. I had a huge malignant ovarian tumour. For a few minutes, I was in a state of shock. I think I missed a few heartbeats. I was shattered and started sobbing. How could it be? I was sure there was some mistake. Never in my wildest dreams could I have thought that I would have cancer. I was informed that the tumour was encapsulated within the ovaries. It had not spread to other organs. I was assured that the cancerous growth had been removed successfully. As a precaution, I would have to undergo a cycle of six chemotherapy sessions. Once again, I was shocked. I knew the side effects and after effects of chemotherapy. I just prayed. I decided I must come to terms with this situation—the sooner the better. I realized that I was lucky that I had not suffered much. The Divine Grace had blessed me. I thanked God for being with me throughout. I went through all the chemotherapy sessions easily. I was very sure of Guruji's grace all the time and feel sure that he was with me throughout, whether as my doctor, or the nurses who took care of me, or as my family and friends who prayed for me. All throughout, I have been thankful to the Divine Grace and have always remembered to express my gratitude to him every day. My recovery from such a major surgery is nothing short of a miracle.

I am absolutely fine now and do the sudarshan kriya regularly. I started working within two months after my surgery. Although I was very weak, my faith in Guruji never faltered. I am positive that the kriya has helped me. I feel healthy and happy and look forward to each day as a blessing. Life seems so beautiful. I feel that I took my life for granted before, and that Guruji gave me a second chance to live.

Sometimes, it does seem as if there is no hope against cancer and that the disease is an inexorable killing machine. However, with a little assistance, Anna Maria Chicola Sanreno from Italy came through victoriously:

After a laparotomy operation, I constantly suffered from bad headaches. I went on a macrobiotic diet. I was also doing *shiatsu*. I felt a little better but had very little energy. Thanks to the ongoing difficulties, I was feeling very depressed. My biggest stroke of luck was that Robert, my son, became an Art of Living Foundation teacher. After a lot of convincing, I did the Art of Living course. Immediately after the course, things started changing for the better. Because of the success of that course, I did a second Art of Living course. In 1999, I took my first advanced course with Guruji. It was the best new year of my life! I was effortlessly doing my pranayama and kriya every day, along with meditation. I am happy and grateful to share that my headaches disappeared! I also had lots of energy! Then came the wonderful DSN course which really gave me another boost of fortune and good health.

The strangest episode occurred on one of my visits to a macrobiotic doctor. He asked me when I had finished my chemo cycle for cancer. When I told him that I had never suffered from cancer, he said that he could see all the signs of a recent cancer. It seemed to have disappeared!

I am now feeling wonderful. I see life with amazement and do my breathing and meditation exercises every day.

I thank Guruji in my prayers and feel his presence near me all the time. I would also like to thank all the Art of Living teachers and the Art of Living students that I met at the courses. Life for me now is very beautiful and full of love.

Recently, an Art of Living follower came to me with his astounding healing experience since he had seen me interviewing people for this book and wished to share his experience with the readers of my book. P. Subramaniam is twenty-eight years old and works in a small-scale engineering unit. He earns a meagre income just sufficient for him and his parents to make ends meet. The nature of the industry in which he is working is unpredictable and there are times when he has to strain himself for long hours to earn adequately to survive, resulting in the wear and tear of his health.

About a year-and-a-half ago he had persistent fever, body pain and difficulty in eating, and was diagnosed with testicular embryonal carcinoma, a malignant germ cell tumour that occurs mostly in the testes. This type of tumour grows rapidly and spreads to the lungs and liver. He underwent orchidectomy, an operation to remove the testicle. This was done to slow down the growth and spreading of the prostate cancer. After the treatment, he managed to carry on. After about a year, in April 2004, he developed similar symptoms of fever, chest discomfort, multiple swelling in the neck and sleeplessness. He was admitted to a local hospital and on diagnosis it was found to be a testicular tumour and lymph node metastasis, a type of cancer that spreads through the blood. He was given three rounds of chemotherapy from April to May 2004.

He did not have sufficient money for the fourth chemotherapy and approached M. Sendhilkumar, an industrialist and an Art of Living volunteer in Coimbatore. Sendhilkumar not only helped him but also put him in the Art of Living part I course. He joined the course on 14 June 2004 and experienced shocks and acute pain in the body after the first sudarshan kriya. He was disinclined to go for the session on the subsequent day. However, he persisted with the second sudarshan kriya which was easier and made him feel relaxed, energized and joyful. Within a week after the completion of the course, he took a haemogram test and the results were encouraging. The doctor asked him to come back after a month and he had another haemogram test on 19 July 2004, which showed vast improvement, and that he had become nearly normal. This was further confirmed by another haemogram test on 21 September 2004 and finally, Subramaniam was back at work with a smile on his face.

Normally, the side effects of chemotherapy are frightening. In Subramaniam's case, the daily practice of pranayama and sudarshan kriya helped eliminate the side effects. He did not feel any exhaustion and was able to work with enthusiasm. He is confident that he has been able to overcome the dreaded disease only because of the Art of Living course and is willing to submit himself to any scientific study on his amazing healing experience.

As I listened to the miracle of this young man's healing, I was moved by the Grace that seemed to have saved this young life.

Other Ailments

Shyam Sardana, an industrialist from Haryana who has started a number of successful companies, has the following story to tell:

> I had been a heart patient since my forties. With my angina, I had to take precautions due to high blood pressure. I had a heart attack at forty-eight, and had been on heavy medication since. I had my first heart surgery at fifty-six when I was diagnosed as having blocked arteries. When my breathing problems started aggravating, I went for a detailed check-up. Tests showed that I was on the brink of death. Every physician I approached gave me a maximum of six months to live. I was advised not

to climb stairs and to not leave my room. I would feel breathless and could hardly walk 1500 yards. While bedridden, I read about the basic course in the Sunday news magazine and on Monday, I contacted an Art of Living teacher, Nityanand. I told Nityanand about my problem and took the basic course the next week. After the course, there was a sea change in my condition. I could move about and my health improved considerably. A month later, I went to the doctor to see if I could travel to Rishikesh to take an advanced course. When I was examined, the doctor was astonished. He asked me, 'Is this the same heart I examined last month?' And I told him, 'Yes, but there's a little change. I have taken up sudarshan kriya in addition to the pills from you!' He had a good laugh. By the time I met Guruji and did the advanced course, I was thoroughly back in shape. I have had no problems till now. I have travelled to Germany and walked up snow clad mountain slopes. I, who was given just six months to live, and that as a vegetable in bed, am now hale and hearty and have been living a normal life for the past three years, just by the grace of Guruji.

Some physical problems do not sound as ominous as cancer or heart attacks, but they can have an equally devastating effect on the body and the mind in the long run. Acidity is one of those psychosomatic problems which usually come with age, stress and wrong food habits, as Abhay Ghanekar of Manama, Bahrain, experienced:

A few months ago when I attended the Art of Living course, my mind was not totally empty. I brought with me a genuine wish that I hoped would be fulfilled. I have lived with a severe acidity problem since childhood. With the passage of time, my condition was only becoming worse. Every other day I would suffer from headaches and vomiting and the problem would spill over to the next day. It was very distressing to me. I took the Art of Living course looking for a final fix since modern medicine hadn't been able to help me. As per the instructions of the teacher, Khurshed, I continued with my sudarshan kriya practice regularly.

After two to three months, my wife and I had a discussion regarding the changes we felt since I had started attending the Art of Living course. She reminded me that I had not complained about having headaches for several days, nor was I vomiting. What she said came as a big surprise to me as I had totally forgotten about my condition! I realized that I had improved my health by simply attending the course. I realized how valuable this was. It was going to save me time, money and a lot of distress, since my visits to the hospital had stopped. However, this part is just what is happening to me at a physical level. With my two eyes, the vision of the world is very limited. I then had to admit that sudarshan kriya must be helping on so many other layers beyond my imagination. Maybe it opens up my inner vision, or unlocks the powers of my 'Third Eye'!

My acidity problem has vanished without a trace. When I do sudarshan kriya on days when I feel a slight headache, I just come out fresh! It is with total amazement that I report my story. No more doctors' visits as the real medicine is in my hands! I am so happy and contented by coming on the right path of the Art of Living Foundation. I am under Guruji's grace forever!

In this day and age of allopathic medicines where every second shop in India is a pharmacy, I often wonder about the harmful side-effects of all these concoctions we pop into our mouths at the slightest sign of discomfort or pain. Could the sudarshan kriya help with the side effects?

This was my question to Simin, an Art of Living teacher from New Zealand who herself had been diagnosed as having familial Mediterranean fever since 1985. This is what she had to say about her first-hand experience with handling the side-effects of medicines with the help of sudarshan kriya:

> I was told that familial Mediterranean fever is a genetic disease with no cure. The medication I was given, Cholchecine, even though helping with the pain and length of pleurisy type attacks, had many unpleasant side-effects. Ever since my basic course, my energy level has been constantly increasing and I have enjoyed very good health. I no longer get painful pleurisy attacks. I am still amazed that the more courses I organize and teach, the more energy I get to carry on my work.

She shared with me stories of people in whom she saw a great improvement or total healing with sudarshan kriya, either during the course or after continued practice, especially in case of illnesses like asthma, epilepsy, high cholesterol level, high blood pressure, high uric acid, heart conditions, diabetes, fibromyalgia and spinal arthritis.

Here is the story of Katie (real name withheld), a woman in her late forties. Katie was diagnosed with systemic lupus when in her early twenties. The disease had ravaged her body and she had only one working, transplanted kidney. All the major joints in her body had been replaced with metal or plastic prostheses (both ankles, both knees, both hips and both wrists). About three years ago, Katie came to the Sheraton Hotel in Baltimore to listen to Sri Sri. The following weekend, she took the basic course and, a month later, travelled all by herself to Canada to take an advanced course with Sri Sri. It must have benefited her, for she went on to take several advanced courses and even attended the DSN course this summer. Such severe medication, along with their side-effects, should by now have taken a major toll on her body. According to her doctors, Katie would have been bedridden and crippled by now. However, with the Guru's grace, she drives to her eight-hour job every day and does not miss even a single satsang.

Anisha, a resident of Mumbai retells us the story she has narrated to many:

> I came to Art of Living because I had had an accident

as a child and I could not breathe properly even after two operations to straighten my nasal partition. After I started performing pranayama, I started breathing easily. Now I have no trouble breathing at night while previously I could not have even a single night's sleep without my dose of Otrivin nasal drops!

And so did R.Velmurugan of Singapore:

I was born and brought up in India and have had sinus problems right from childhood. When exposed to even a little dust, I would sneeze at least ten times before returning to normal breathing. Due to this, I would regularly fall prey to colds and coughs, as if I had a regular visitor to my system, whether I liked it or not. I made up my mind to attend the Art of Living course since I had heard so much about the benefits of sudarshan kriya and the pranayama exercises for my kind of problem. On the fourth day of attending the course, I was reading my newspaper while my wife was cleaning one of the dusty racks. She forgot to ask me to step out of the room as she always used to. To my surprise, I did not sneeze as I usually did. My wife also noticed this change. That was the day my sinus difficulties left me forever! We know that it is Guruji's grace that has enveloped us. We have been doing sudarshan kriya ever since then and I am very happy to say that there is no sign of sinus trouble with me.

Sudarshan kriya has also proved to have been extremely effective for those suffering from asthma, a powerful psychosomatic disease, which leaves many of us crippled and helpless.

Here is what Ria Culloty told me as we talked:

Last November, I decided I really wanted to be free of asthma and wondered if the Art of Living course might be able to help in this area. On the second day of the course, I didn't use the Ventilin puffer. This wasn't really a decision I made, rather I 'forgot' to use it in the morning. By day four of the course, I realized that I wasn't using the puffer and haven't used it since. Earlier, it had got to the point where I had started keeping Ventilin in my car, my purse, my workplace and various places at home. It wasn't that my asthma was that bad, but it was more for convenience. Anyway, prior to the course, I used to have two puffs, twice a day. Since then, I have not had to use Ventilin at all! This has been a blessing!

One of the diseases of our times, caused by the stress of keeping up with life, running from one appointment to the other, being on the move in restless activity and never giving rest to our body or mind, is a funny sickness called chronic fatigue syndrome. This is the story of N. Narayanan from Chennai:

While being treated for TB for a whole year with heavy antibiotics, I developed severe weakness and fatigue which continued even after I stopped the medicines. For more than fifteen months after the TB treatment, I continued suffering from acute fatigue. I could not do my regular exercises and could not work in office for more than four hours a day. I would feel tired and sapped of energy even after taking a full day's rest. This physical disability had affected my mental strength too. I started going into depression. My immune system also got weakened. I used to get a sore throat, cold and cough almost every month and, at times, it would continue for two to three weeks.

A couple of years ago, I got an opportunity to attend the basic course. I was amazed after doing the very first sudarshan kriya. There was a surge of an unusual energy in my body and mind. In the next one month, I could see a great change in my energy levels. The severity of fatigue and sore throat had come down. And after one year, I had almost got back to normal. Now, after two years, I can confidently say that I have not experienced the old horrendous state of fatigue ever since I joined the course. My immune system has normalized and my mental state has bounced back to its enthusiastic self.

I always had a doubt that this cure was temporary. That's why I hesitated to even share my experience with you earlier. However, now I am confident that I have recovered from this funny and troublesome disease. I have not even an iota of doubt that this cure is only due to sudarshan kriya since I did not take any other treatment for my problem.

Ailments Afflicting Women

Women have had some strong healing experiences with the sudarshan kriya, especially for problems faced by them as their bodies go through hormonal changes every month and later experience other changes in their body as they come closer to menopause. Many suffer from fibroids and are forced to have their uterus removed, an operation which leaves both physical and psychological scars, as described by this anonymous devotee:

> Two years ago, I needed surgery to remove my uterus. The doctor was not competent enough and damaged the wall of my bladder and affected my kidney. After the surgery, the abdominal pain remained, and in the next three months it only worsened. I decided to come to India for better medical treatment. A scan showed a foreign body lodged in my abdomen—a small clip left by the surgeon during the previous operation! The doctors wanted to perform another surgery to remove the object. However, I decided to wait till Guruji's return from Germany and have his *darshan* before going ahead with the operation. As the pain grew worse, and based on the doctors' prognosis, I resigned myself to the surgery. I spoke to Gurudev over the telephone and he asked me to do a particular meditation. On the seventh morning, I had to go for a pre-operative scan.

The next morning, Guruji arrived and I went for a *pooja* at the ashram before going to collect the report. When I reached the medical centre, I found that the doctors were incredulous; there was no trace of the object. The clip had completely disappeared!

In today's world, what we are worth is measured by how we look and dress. Many a person has fallen into the trap to remain young and beautiful at whatever cost. We go to extremes to achieve this. However, the obsession with remaining slim by following crash diets has devastating effects on our bodies, as Manju K. from Jakarta, Indonesia, discovered:

> I still remember those days when I was preparing myself to be an MTV VJ. Physically, it was taking a toll on me. I abused my body to its very being. The desire to fit into the MTV image of a perfect, slim body made me go on various diets and I spent hours in the gym. As a result, I often fell sick, was admitted to the hospital, and the doctors frequently gave me large doses of antibiotics since my immune system had completely given up. It is funny, but very few people know what actually goes on in the minds of people who are going through bulimia. The person's mind would be thinking about food throughout the day and dreaming about it too. It is a condition that completely wrecks one's mind and of course, body. Then I met Guruji and spent some time at the ashram. He would talk to me patiently about my eating habits; he would inquire about the functioning of my stomach, and actually tell me what to do next and how. On the face of it, I looked very healthy and beautiful, but nobody knew the turmoil within me. It is the kriya and all the other cleansing processes which have kept me going. Before meeting Gurudev, life was an effort, now it is effortless. If a fish is asked to narrate the vastness of an ocean or to describe its greatness, will it be able to put it into words?

Addictions

Whoever has tried, unsuccessfully, to kick the habit of smoking cigarettes will easily relate to this testimony by Robert C. of Salisbury, MD, USA. This is his letter, which he aptly titled 'A Craving for Healthy Living':

> I realized I was addicted to cigarettes when my addiction got to the point where I had to have a cigarette or would get a headache. It was more than just a game now. I asked myself, 'How could someone who did yoga and sudarshan kriya end up getting addicted to cigarettes?' I thought I could just have one every once in a while and enjoy cigarettes occasionally. I had been mildly addicted once before (fourteen years before), but quit 'cold turkey' without any difficulty.
>
> Living in Annapolis, Maryland, working down in the yacht yards, I played all the mental games of someone who thinks they are getting somewhere on the road to quitting a bad habit from which they had nothing to gain. I was cutting down to one a day or three a day or skipping a day, only to relapse. Skipping days only gave me headaches! Then I would binge on two, three, or even five, if things got really hectic. I would cut it down to maybe three a week and then relapse again to three a day.
>
> One day in January 2007, sitting on my screened-in porch, I had the uncontrollable urge again. It usually hit hardest in the morning when the prana was low and I wanted a boost. I knew in my mind that the only way to quit was to not do it again, even once; but it had become like a sexual desire, consuming all, so that every conscious thought filtered through the addiction. I put the cigarette in my mouth really knowing that if I was ever going to quit and be successful, I had to be willing to never smoke a cigarette again in my life. The cigarette remained in my mouth that morning for some time without being lit as I reflected over the sobering thought of never smoking another cigarette in my life.

I love the taste of a cigarette, the buzz of the nicotine. I also knew what it was doing to my health and how the addiction was altering my consciousness. I really wanted to quit smoking! That morning I gave it everything I had to consciously decide not to light that cigarette. It sat in my mouth, as I smelled a familiar fragrance, like flowers or something.

Suddenly I felt Guruji's robe brush against the back of my arm, just above the elbow. He said softly, lovingly and matter-of-factly into my ear, 'You can drop this.' His presence was very strong with me. Instead of thinking about what I was giving up, I focussed on what it would be like to be free of this addiction, to never smoke again! After five minutes of the two parts of my divided mind fighting, the side of me that really wanted to quit won. I naturally took the cigarette out of my mouth and placed it in the ashtray. I am happy to say that I have not smoked even a single cigarette since then! Guruji had helped tip the balance for me, taking seven steps to each that I took. Not only did I feel extremely loved, but I felt he really had an eye on me and knew what I was going through in my life. He has always helped me with difficult situations. As long as I took the first step with the intention of reaching a goal, he was right there with me. His loving encouragement helped me through.

If I have learnt anything from him, it is: *This* is all *me* and whatever happens is my decision ... to take charge and be the boss of this mind, body and creation. Even the Guru cannot save me unless I do it first! Jai Gurudev! Victory to the One Big Mind!

Along with our lifestyle and problems such as drinking and smoking, another challenge is drugs. Drug addiction begins, again, as a way to keep up with our peers, but later becomes such an addiction that it becomes a struggle for both the mind and the body to break the habit. However for Musa Zungu, a twenty-three-year-old from South Africa, getting latched to drugs was a way to forget a traumatic experience, rather than peer pressure:

I began studying for a Bachelor of Education degree three years ago. However, I couldn't finish my degree because I got mugged on the way to University. The thugs took away everything I had. From that point, my life went down, I started drinking, smoking, and doing drugs. I was drinking and doping from Monday to Sunday to escape from the world, to make my mind forget the incident.

Last year, I did the Art of Living course and then went to the YLTP. We had a great teacher, Vikram. He was always there for us and acted as a role model. He taught me to take control of my life. He taught me how to forgive. I used to say that I would never forgive the people who did bad things to me. I am more confident about myself, and have this vavavoom! Before doing YLTP phase II, I didn't drink for six weeks. It made me realize that there are better things in life than killing yourself slowly but surely. I was taught how to become an agent of change in my community. Now, I can be with people who drink alcohol and drink water or juice in their company. I've given up smoking and doing drugs. With Art of Living, one feels blessed. I feel that I must have done something good in the past to be fortunate enough get this knowledge and be a part of the Art of Living.

AIDS

HIV/AIDS is the curse of our times along with cancer and though a cure for it is still to be found, people who are afflicted with this disease seem to benefit from doing pranayama and sudarshan kriya. Though I personally don't think that sudarshan kriya can cure AIDS, I am sure the fact that the body is receiving positive energy from the practice helps, because prana helps to eliminate toxins and boosts the body's ability to fight aliments. David M. from Pennsylvania, who was diagnosed with HIV at the prime of his life, has this to share with us:

I was lucky enough to be on the forty-day HIV course. It gave me a spiritual experience beyond anything I can put into words. I now feel that Gurudev is with me in my heart wherever I go. I would not have been caught dead saying something like that five years ago. Gurudev has opened the door of spirituality, devotion and love for me. I have been living with HIV for about fifteen years, and thanks to his grace, I am fine and healthy.

Not all of us have experienced these dramatic healings. At times, it is enough that someone close to you experiences the wonders of sudarshan kriya to make your belief stronger, as Ramola narrates:

Yajna Bheemah, a four-year-old girl, had an accident, wherein a beam got stuck in her trachea and she had a cardiac arrest. Her brain got damaged due to the unavailability of oxygen. This affected the posterior lobes of her brain. She lost all her neurological abilities and eyesight. Doctors said that she would not be able to walk or see again. After her parents made her take part in the part I course, Yajna started standing, walking and running. Once she took the part II course, she started distinguishing between colours! Now she is able to see objects that are at a distance of about four feet and her condition is improving by the day!

I still have doubts in my mind. Nevertheless, it seems to me that the one thread that runs through all these healings and what weaves all these stories into a beautiful tapestry of joy and peace is what in India is called 'the Grace'. Yes, pranayama and sudarshan kriya are the instruments through which the grace flows and heals the many lives that come in contact with it. For many, the miracle of healing—not only of the body, but also of the mind and the soul—has happened just by being around the Master.

Christ as a Healer

The message of Christ is one of love, of respecting other cultures and creeds. The divine has manifested itself down the ages under different names and identities, whether it is Buddha, Krishna or Mohamed or Christ. Today, many Christians have gone through the Art of Living course and have been transformed. The beautiful thing is that they have not turned their back on their religion, but on the contrary have become better Christians, thanks to Sri Sri. Andrew Jones, an American priest, is certainly one of them. This is what he wrote to Gurudev:

> Dearest Gurudev, as a priest, I have chosen to see you as the living Christ, and I imagine that those who saw Jesus must have experienced Him just as we experience you now. I always see you at the altar and ask for your blessings and presence during the Mass. God, Guru and Self are indeed all the same; yet the Guru is very special because he is God in a tangible body. We are blessed and thankful to have your love. I ask for your continued blessings in life, in all my roles, so that I may be blessed and grow to become Nobody and then become Everybody. I wish to live in bliss and share it with others, bless and love others with the strength and unity of God, Guru and Self. You are as close to me as my heart. But I want more! I want nothing less than to be you!

Christ the 'Avatar of Love', performed many miracles on those who were suffering. We have all heard the story of a man paralyzed for life who walked at the injunction of Jesus Christ. Sri Sri did not even need to do that according to Dr Saran, a paediatrician from Mongolia:

> When Guruji was in Ulaan Bator on a state visit, we were amazed at the devotion and connectedness of the Mongolian people, most of whom were seeing him for

the first time. Heads bowed and eyes filled with tears, they came in hundreds to have a glimpse of the 'Living God' as they addressed him. In the crowd was a lady who had been paralyzed and bedridden for years. When she saw Guruji's photo in the newspaper, she immediately recognized him as her guru, rose from her bed and walked to the satsang for his darshan, where she shared her healing experience as we looked on in wonder. There was also a child who had lost his hearing and speaking abilities at the age of three, due to wrong medication. A lama had predicted that at the age of twelve, he would be cured by a holy man from abroad. And this is exactly what happened! The divine instruments change through the ages but the healing continues!

Chapter Four

Healing the Mind

Depression, Anxiety and Psychological Disorders

Depression is one of the most widespread emotional problems of our times. Although the term itself is commonly used to describe a temporary mood when one feels 'blue', clinical depression is a serious and often disabling condition. The normal stresses of life—ranging from, say, an argument with a friend or poor performance in a test to a break-up or not being chosen for a team—can lead to natural feelings of sadness, hurt, disappointment or grief that could make anyone feel low every once in a while. However, these reactions are usually brief and go away with a little time and care. Clinical depression, on the other hand, is much more than an occasional down-in-the-dumps feeling. It is a strong mood involving sadness, discouragement, despair or hopelessness that lasts for weeks, months or even longer, affecting a person's very outlook and behaviour and interfering with his ability to participate in normal activities.

Depression can be mild or severe. People with depression tend to have negative and self-critical thoughts and often, despite their true value, feel worthless and unloved. Because of such feelings of sadness and low energy, people with depression may pull away from those around them or from activities they once enjoyed. This usually makes them feel lonelier and more isolated, aggravating the depression and negative thinking. At its worst, depression can create such feelings of despair that a person even contemplates suicide. It can cause psychosomatic symptoms as well, such as an upset stomach, loss of appetite, weight gain or loss, headaches and sleeping problems.

Why Do People Get Depressed?

There is no single cause for depression. Many factors play a role, including genetics, environment, life events, medical conditions and the way people react to things that happen in their lives.

Genetics

Research shows that depression runs in families and that some people inherit genes that make them susceptible to depression. However, not everyone who has the genetic make-up for depression gets depressed, and many people who have no family history of depression develop the condition. So, although genes are a factor, they aren't the sole cause of depression.

Life Events

From the moment we enter the world, crying in anguish with our first breath, to our last whiff of breath, life is a constant struggle to assert ourselves, defend our territory and protect our values and dear ones. Insecurity is our lot. The death of a family member or a dear friend can go beyond normal grief and may lead to depression, as can other difficult life events, such as when parents separate, get divorced or remarry.

Family and Social Environment

In many cases, depression may stem from a negative or stressful family atmosphere. Such situations may include poverty, violence (both physical and mental) or even a general feeling of disconnect with the family or community. A sustained dip in the mood, no matter how trivial the cause, should not be left unchecked since it may lead to a serious state of depression.

Substance Abuse

Substance abuse is also known to cause chemical changes in the brain, affecting one's mood. Some drugs are known to alter the constitution of the brain and to have depressant effects too. The isolation and other negative consequences of substance abuse only serve to aggravate the problem.

Medical Conditions

Certain medical conditions can affect hormone balance and therefore have a negative effect on mood. Some conditions, such as hypothyroidism, are known to cause depression in some people. However, the depression usually disappears when these medical conditions are diagnosed and treated. In case of children, undiagnosed learning disabilities may adversely affect grades in school while hormonal changes might affect mood, or physical illness might present challenges or setbacks. This may again lead to depression.

What Happens in the Brain When Someone Is Depressed?

Depression involves the brain's delicate chemistry, especially chemicals called neurotransmitters. These chemicals help send messages between nerve cells in the brain. Certain neurotransmitters regulate our mood, and if they run low, people can become depressed, anxious and stressed. Stress can also affect the balance of neurotransmitters and lead to depression. Even in the West, it is now generally accepted that traditional techniques of yoga and pranayama improve mental health. The effects of stress and depression on physical and mental health are far-reaching. Anxiety and depression have been found to aggravate the progression of serious diseases like cancer, HIV, asthma and cardiovascular ailments. Psychoneuroimmunology (PNI) is the science that deals with these problems. Sudarshan kriya and related breathing techniques have been found to have remarkable therapeutic benefits.

Medical Research on Depression, Addiction, etc.

The National Institute of Mental Health and Neurosciences (NIMHANS), Bangalore, and the All India Institute of Medical Sciences (AIIMS), Delhi, have been carrying out research on sudarshan kriya and its effects. Clinical trials at NIMHANS showed that regular practice of sudarshan kriya is as effective as the established tricyclic anti-depressant drug, Imipramine (Depsonil, Antidep). Dr Gangadhar, who carried out these studies systematically with different groups of patients using different techniques, reached the same conclusion in all cases—that the exercises lead to certain neurophysiological changes that help cure depression.

For instance, in one study he randomly put patients of acute depression through shock therapy, drugs or breathing exercises. The final results showed that although the results were best with shock therapy, the breathing exercises gave better results as compared to drugs.

In another study, he put forty-six patients of chronic depression on breathing exercises. At the end of a three month trial, as many as twenty-six of them who had been practising it regularly showed improvement. About 150 patients were studied by this method, and the findings published in various national and international journals.

It was also reported that the distorted dream-stage EEG brainwave patterns of patients of depression improved significantly with the practice of pranayama and sudarshan kriya. People with depression have a particular EEG brainwave abnormality that can be measured by the P300 ERP amplitude. When P300 was post-tested on day ninety, it had returned to normal (it was indistinguishable from normal controls) and they remained free of depressive symptoms. There was a reduction in REM latency onset and an improvement in NREM stages. About 70 per cent of the patients who had completed the programme experienced a reduction in depression, when tested after one month and three months. Blood analysis revealed statistically significant elevation of plasma prolactin levels after the very first sudarshan kriya session. This is important since elevated plasma prolactin is crucial in producing an anti-depressant response. Cortisol (a stress hormone) levels remained stable, indicating that the practice of sudarshan kriya is not stressful.

Researcher Dr A. Vedamurthachar found that this exercise proved effective at the de-addiction unit as well, and the thirty alcoholics who had agreed to participate in the study were found to have reduced levels of depression and anxiety afterwards.

We have seen over and over again how pranayama and sudarshan kriya have helped people in even the most desperate situations of their lives. Laura from Houston, Texas, discovered the power of the sudarshan kriya after an attempt at taking her own life:

> A friend suggested I take the course after unsuccessful attempts at suicide. I reluctantly agreed and had another friend drive me to the course because I was sure I was going to chicken out. I only stayed because our teacher Krishna T. said that if we missed any course classes, then the whole group would miss out as he would not continue. One day we waited over an hour for someone who was reluctant to come back. So I knew Krishna T. was serious. I stayed on. However, I was glad when it was over and did not do any sadhana for over a year.
>
> During that time, I fell into a deep depression and did not work for practically eight months, never leaving my apartment where I ate fast food, watched TV and slept. The same friend who had introduced me to Art of Living

asked if I was breathing and I replied that I wasn't. At the same time, Krishna T. kept calling me and inviting me back. That was the last thing on my mind, of course. I had serious problems to overcome which I thought breathing could not help me. But finally, one day, I fell on my knees and cried out for help and began to do kriya again, slowly and with a lot of effort.

Today, sadhana, satsang and seva have literally saved my life. Gone are the suicidal thoughts, the suicide attempts, the depression, the anti-depressants and the therapy. I work now and haven't missed a day at office in over seven months. And of course, I do my kriya every day without fail. Guruji has saved me and continues to take me higher and higher in knowledge and truth, each passing day.

I have nothing with which to repay him, so I offer my life and take total refuge in him, come what may.

While the sudarshan kriya helps in releasing anger and frustration and awakening love, thus bringing peace to our mind and body, Sri Sri Ravi Shankar also emphasizes seva and satsang as powerful tools for healing.

Your body is made up of atoms. Being with this truth kindles energy in you and elevates your consciousness. When you sing *bhajans* at satsang, the energy of the sounds gets absorbed into every atom of your body. Just as a microphone absorbs sound and converts it into electricity, the body absorbs sound and converts it into consciousness. When you sit in satsang, your entire body gets soaked in energy and transformation happens. If you sit and listen to gossip or violent music, then that gets absorbed by your body too. But when you hear knowledge, or chant with all your heart, your consciousness is elevated.

Along with satsang, when we lose ourselves in seva, forgetting everything but the need to serve, healing takes place without effort. Arvind C. of Bulawayo, Zimbabwe, recalls how he rediscovered himself through the healing breath and the power of satsang:

> I did my first Art of Living course with Nitin Limaye, one of the senior Art of Living teachers, while undergoing psychiatric treatment for chronic bipolar clinical depression. Although on a cocktail of prescribed anti-depressant drugs, thoughts of committing suicide were my constant companion. In addition, I had been smoking twenty cigarettes a day for close to twenty-five years.
>
> After the course, a major shift happened. I was so filled with love and joy that I went around town hugging almost everyone I knew. I knew no other way to express myself. In retrospect, I think people were convinced that I had indeed finally 'lost my marbles'.
>
> Three days after the course, I quit smoking. I realize now that it was only through Guruji's grace that something miraculous like this could happen. I suffered zero withdrawal symptoms. Like an overripe fruit, the habit just dropped out of my life.
>
> I continued to do my routine of sudarshan kriya at home every morning. Within three months after the course, under the psychiatrist's supervision, I quit taking anti-depressant drugs. I continued my home kriya routine and attended the Friday evening follow-up sessions. A year later, I repeated the Art of Living course and followed that with an advanced course facilitated by Urmila Devi Baumann from the German ashram. It was only after this course that I truly felt that Guruji had become 'my' Guru.
>
> Shortly after the advanced course, I initiated a weekly Art of Living satsang to be held every Thursday evening. There are several satsang groups of long standing in Bulawayo and I pressed on to sing praises of my Guru every Thursday. From small beginnings, where just a handful of people would turn up, these are now well attended and in fact fully attended throughout the year.

Once again, I believe it is only through Guruji's grace that this has happened.

It was only after I did the advanced course that my wife, Bhakti, began to pay attention to what was happening to me. She was understandably sceptical as she had seen me go through highs ad lows before. Furthermore, it is certainly not easy to live with a clinically depressed person. Bhakti did eventually take the Art of Living course and repeated it a year later. She has moved from strength to strength on this wonderful path. At present, she is the only Art of Living course teacher in Zimbabwe.

For some strange reason, I just stopped doing my home routine of sudarshan kriya on a daily basis. Stresses started building up and before I knew it I was depressed. I foolishly took to smoking again. Soon, I was back on Prozac for my depression. Bhakti and Nitin Limaye convinced me that I must do my first DSN course. It seems to me that Guruji's *sankalpa* that I did not need medication seemed to work the magic once again. I have been off my medication ever since. I regret not having told Guruji that I had also started smoking again.

After the DSN course, I have been regular with my daily home routine, attending satsangs and the weekly follow-up sudarshan kriya. A year later, I went to the Bangalore ashram to do the teacher training course. I felt that I did not deserve the opportunity due to my smoking problem. Yet, through Guruji's grace and the encouragement of the recommending teacher, it happened.

During the TTC I course, I decided against submitting my experience due to my ongoing smoking problem, although I did not have a single thought for a cigarette and had no craving whatsoever. Soon after the TTC I course, that habit arose and I could think of nothing else but a cigarette. I feel I had spurned Guruji's offer to help me finally quit the habit. Even as I write this, I have not quit smoking.

My advice to smokers who do the Art of Living course and then quit smoking is to continue the daily practice of sudarshan kriya and to never take even a puff of a cigarette. There is no such thing as 'just one puff' or 'just one cigarette'. It is a choking chain reaction.

I no longer need the anti-depressant medication. I encourage others to take the Art of Living course... why take Prozac when a daily dose of sudarshan kriya will do the trick?

Over and again, one hears the refrain of people who have done the Art of Living course experiencing a great opening of the heart and feelings of love and belonging, which lead them to service or seva. The participants are inspired to volunteer, to partake in the service projects with enthusiasm, where service is performed as an expression of joy and love, creating a global wave of love, celebration and belonging.

This is what a participant had to say about her experiences:

I was going through a very rough patch in my life. I'd just lost my father to cancer and my relationship with my boyfriend was also on the wane. I was in really bad shape. There were infrequent smiles on my face, infrequent meetings with friends and not a lot of activity in my life. I wasn't sleeping well and I felt reluctant to get out of bed every morning. I went to my doctor and became one of the millions on anti-depressants.

This was my existence until a friend of mine who had taken the Art of Living course insisted that I do it too. After months of absolute harassment, I decided that I would take the course only to see what sort of cult he had gotten himself into. I decided that my last act as his friend would be to see what sort of de-programming he would need. The first night, we learnt something strange called 'pranayama'. It was more than foreign to me, but it seemed harmless enough, so I participated. That night I slept better than I had in at least ten years. So I decided to show up for the course the next night.

On Saturday we did this breathing technique called sudarshan kriya. I found it very difficult to do. I peeked at what was going on around in the room, basically minding everyone's business but mine. But even though I had my eyes open most of the time, not keeping the rhythm, I still felt really good afterwards. There was this resting period at the end which seemed to last an eternity. Someone made some funny noise in the room and that was it. We laughed for what seemed like an hour. That afternoon I did many things which I had not done in years. I felt energized, and a sense of peacefulness I had never felt before permeated me. Most importantly, I slept the deepest I had in years.

The next day we did the sudarshan kriya again. But this time I decided that I would keep my eyes closed and see what happens. It seemed so much easier this time. I felt extraordinarily different when I opened my eyes. I noticed the sky through the open window, and it was as if it were the very first time that I had seen the sky in my life! Then I looked around the room and made real eye contact with people after I don't know how long. Their eyes were so bright, so beautiful. I just fell in love with each and every one of them.

Shortly after taking the course, I was able to stop taking anti-depressants. This was just the beginning. From the moment I opened my eyes after the second sudarshan kriya, I realized that the entire fabric of my life had changed, and I began living again! Smiles returned to my face. Kindness and warmth began to radiate from my heart to others. My life began to transform from one of bitterness and sadness to one of richness and beauty. I began experiencing more beauty and love than I had ever experienced before. The purpose of my life became clear, and a contentment I had never known overcame me. I discovered that my greatest joy came through being of service to others.

I have no words which can accurately capture the magnitude of the gratitude I feel for Guruji. I am on this

planet because of his grace and unconditional love. I am
here for him, because of him, to serve him ...

Joy and love, found through service to those in need, helped
Diana heal her mind. She had spent the last six months in the
Bangalore ashram, involved in the empowerment programmes
for women, when I met her. Working with these simple, down-
to-earth women had helped to heal and empower her in turn. It
was a beautiful example of how each supported the other—she
had taught them a skill and they had taught her the skills to live
life fully!

The Mind

The mind is the master of the physical being. However, one
does not always use the mind in the correct manner. It has a
considerable power over the body. One often misuses its power
and as a result makes the body ill. As soon as things start going
wrong, the mind begins to shape and imagine all kinds of possible
catastrophes. It tricks us into taking actions that are detrimental
to our body and soul. At times like this, instead of letting the mind
do its disastrous work, one should use one's faculties to imagine
favourable formations, and do such exercises as telling oneself
that this is just a passing disturbance, thus giving confidence to
the body and mind to overcome the difficulty. It helps the body
enter a real state of receptivity, and achieve wonderful results.

It is never too late to help ourselves to heal. India's ancient texts
offer many tools to help develop and discover the hidden powers
within us which enable us to heal our own bodies and minds.

The mantra has infinite value as a healing tool. You choose
your mantra as a spontaneous expression of your aspiration;
it may be a single word, two or three words or a sentence, but
it must be a sound which awakens in you a certain condition.
You call on it in a moment of difficulty, and it springs up like

magic, to produce wonderful results. But we must make a habit of repeating it every day, so that in times of difficulty the mantra comes spontaneously as a protection.

One evening at the dinning hall, I sat with Joe Hardy, a teacher from England, and we got into a conversation regarding meditation. I shared with him how, in the midst of a great storm, Philip had taught Namrita and me the Sahaj Samadhi meditation, a simple process with a mantra that shuns all effort. I found it a great help in improving my meditation since it leads one to the stillness and silence of one's being. I had been meditating or trying to for many years and it dawned on me that this silence, this awareness of the self, is not something that one can strive for or achieve by 'doing', because it is not a goal outside one's self. Sahaj meditation is surrender—a relinquishing of all trying, a falling into yourself, the experience of ultimate relaxation.

Joe then shared a story about a young woman in England, one of his students called Pat, who was greatly helped by the Art of Living techniques and Sahaj meditation.

> Pat was going through a year of deep depression, bordering on a nervous breakdown. She had been to doctors, therapists and a psychiatrist without any results. Diagnosed with acute anxiety, her health was at a low ebb, both mentally and physically. In her own words she was a 'wreck'. It was in this state that she came to do the Art of Living part I course. During the course she was able to relax and unwind for the first time in many months. At the end of the workshop, she was much improved and our regular chats had established a contact. I encouraged her to keep in touch and call if she had any problems.
>
> Just over a week had passed after the course when I heard Pat on the other side of the telephone line, weeping inconsolably. Her depression had returned with a vengeance. She kept crying, 'I can't take it any more,' and wanted to end it all.
>
> I said, 'Okay, but first come and have a cup of tea. Then we will see.'

Pat came to the centre in great distress, clutching her stomach in pain. She was in obvious agony, both mentally and physically. Her doctor had told her she had an inflamed bowel. She was on the verge of suicide. She unloaded her latest problems over a cup of tea. I then asked her to lie down on the couch and relax, close her eyes and let go of everything. I lead her gently into a deep meditation for thirty minutes. I watched as the strain left her face.

Suddenly she sat up and cried, 'The pain is gone. I can't feel a thing. It's wonderful!'

The great cloud that she had come with had lifted. She was cured of the pain. Her mental anguish had vanished. I then taught her the Sahaj meditation so that she could practise it daily.

Pat has taken up voluntary work at a local school. Her dark days are over. She has found an inner strength and looks and feels like a new person.

The inner journey is the unsurpassed adventure of one's life. It is not something that can be mapped out from a book, but needs competent guidance. It is for this that Sri Sri, and so many before him, came to guide us to take refuge in the Divine. The Divine brings the soothing touch to life which has otherwise been moving in many directions. To take refuge in the Divine brings total rest.

Stress

Stress is the bane of the modern era, creating an imbalance between the body and mind, which in turn leads to a lowering of our resistance to disease and weakening of our immune system. Most medical problems today are triggered or aggravated by stress. While it is easy to be a victim of stress, kicking the habit of inviting stress and being stres-free through the day may require some effort. The path of least resistance is to take stress relievers, drugs that are freely sold over-the-counter and generously recommended by general practitioners as antidotes for depression, tension and ailments like ulcer, asthma, cholesterol and cancer. Drugs, however, treat the symptoms and not the root cause of problems.

As mentioned earlier, research done by AIIMS, Delhi, has proven that sudarshan kriya and pranayama reduced serum cortisol levels—an indicator of stress—in the blood more effectively than listening to classical music. As Dr Kochupillai of AIIMS says, 'When one is going through a stressful situation, the whole physiology, the brain and endocrine system, is influenced negatively. Breathing techniques such as pranayama and sudarshan kriya establish a positive body–mind relationship. Removal of negative thoughts and tensions leads to a positive and healthy physiology.'

This is powerfully expressed by our friend Beatriz Goyoaga from Argentina:

> For nine years, the stress of my job as department head of a press office took its toll on my body. My position as supervisor of fourteen publications, and my eagerness to do more and more, had driven my mind and body to a tremendous precipice from where I would have never stepped back if it had not been for sudarshan kriya.
>
> The stress in which I was living had put my immune system down to its lowest level. I was not only contracting all kinds of small illnesses, but had also contracted a serious and painful herpes virus. HPV is well-known to have a high risk of turning into cancer if the virus sets in the uterus.
>
> For five years, the disease tormented me. Blisters and sores covered my body, especially the mucous membranes. They disappeared at times, but remained dormant only to return more virulent every time my stress levels rose.
>
> Doctors had given me all kinds of highly expensive virus treatments and aloe creams. I was also placed on pills and vitamins to raise my immunity levels, but to no

avail. My mouth, lips, tongue and throat were sometimes so blistered that I could barely talk or swallow.

The virus got stronger and stronger and nothing seemed to help relieve the pain and misery. Even my gynaecologist, a well-known and respected physician in Buenos Aires, had given up on me. She sent me to seek psychotherapy and alternative medicine to see whether my health could improve.

It was by coincidence, or so I thought, that after my third day of psychoanalysis, I took the Art of Living course. Within a few weeks of regularly performing sudarshan kriya, I stopped my visits to the psychoanalyst. The herpes ulcers have completely disappeared! Initially I thought that the virus would come back in some time, as it usually did. But it has been three years since I last had any pain or symptoms. I haven't felt the need to take any medicine either. I feel my defence system has become so strong that whenever the HPV virus manifests itself, my body's defences attack it successfully and naturally. I have much gratitude for my healing! My doctor was so amazed when I told her of the situation that she herself decided to take the course. She now tells all her patients to come and take it themselves!

While sudarshan kriya is relatively new as a breathing technique, pranayama is an ancient yogic breathing technique. Dr Kochupillai, who is an expert in yogic breathing techniques herself, says, 'With regular pranayama, the body, mind and emotional activities start getting harmonized. The endocrine system and brain waves also become synchronized.'

According to Dr Manvir Bhatia, Associate Professor at the Department of Neurology, AIIMS, 'Yogic breathing exercises prevent stress-related neurological disorders like tension headaches, non-epileptic seizures and sleeping disorders. Of all headaches, the share of headache caused by tension is 70 per cent. This occurs mainly due to stress at office or home.'

This observation is validated by the experience of Sabina from Toronto, Canada, who suffered tremendously from anxiety attacks and stress-induced headaches. Here, she narrates the story of her journey from stress to happiness:

> In August, I started experiencing severe stress-related headaches. I contacted my general physician who was not able to pinpoint the cause. So I was referred for more extensive examinations, including a brain scan. No anomalies were detected. I was prescribed Tylenol with an added sedative, but these did not help much. After a month, the headaches went from periodic to continuous throughout the day. Other symptoms, such as crying, started. Since the doctor suspected depression, I scheduled an appointment with a psychiatrist. The crying got worse and panic attacks began. I could not stay in a closed room without getting panic attacks and shortness of breath. As the panic attacks increased, I had difficulty even boarding a bus. At the entrance to the subway, I would suddenly feel dizzy and would not dare enter.
>
> In October, I quit my job. The symptoms were too much to handle with work. During my November appointment, my psychiatrist prescribed Paxil. That appeared to help and, within a month, I started feeling much better. I got a new job. With the help of my family, I began going out, even getting on the subway again. I felt okay again. I found myself pleasantly engrossed in my work. By March next year, I gradually began reducing the dosage of Paxil.
>
> In June, personal and work issues cropped up. I quit my job and stayed at home. After a week, I was back to the old symptoms: all-night crying bouts; a constant flow of negative thoughts; no interest in life. By September, I left for an extended vacation without seeing the psychiatrist again.
>
> While on vacation, I repeated the Art of Living course. I had done the course two years earlier, but had never practised the techniques. Even after repeating the course, I did not proactively practise the Art of Living breathing techniques that I had learnt.

In November, the panic attacks resumed. Still on my long vacation, I saw a nearby doctor who prescribed Zoloft at a stronger dosage than the previous Paxil prescriptions. I lost all interest in life, feeling so low that I had forgotten what it was like to be normal. Desperate for relief, I resorted to doing kriya at home. I did it every day while I continued the prescribed medication.

Four weeks later, I experienced three days of heavy crying with a feeling of 'going mad'. Those three days were followed by what can only be described as a miraculous cure. I felt light and happy! For the first time in a year and a half, I did not cry for a full 24 hours. I really felt happy again and did not have to force myself to smile. The emotional and physical healing had begun!

In December, I came home again, determined to start afresh. I consulted my former psychiatrist and kept up the schedule of frequent appointments. My medications were reduced to half dosage after twenty days, and a quarter dose after another fifteen days. I continue at the quarter dose, with the psychiatrist's permission to stop any time! What a change!

I am planning to meet Guruji soon. For the first time in my life, I have the confidence to say that I will never be depressed again.

I would like to end my story with a poem:

Mind, Body and Soul

The mind, both a powerful tool
And a weapon of destruction.
When it decided to act upon itself
It did so with a vengeance so evil that it nearly killed itself.
The pain was disguised,
So no one could see it,
No one could feel it.
The body was burning in isolation.

Life was reduced to a saga of endless suffering.
But there was a soul—a human one—that refused to die!
A *diya* of compassion lit up.
Sudarshan kriya was the beginning.
Layers unravelled and fell to ashes.
Truth revealed itself.
The mind, a powerful tool,
Began to act upon itself.
This time, with the mercy of a father,
And the warmth of a mother.
Now mind, body and soul, healed and restored,
Depression seems like such a joke!

Chapter Five

Conflict Resolution

From negotiating for peace in Sri Lanka to transforming misguided youth in Kashmir to taming the fire of hatred in the Balkans, the volunteers of the Art of Living, inspired by the example of Sri Sri Ravi Shankar, are busy building bridges between conflicting groups.

Shifting the focus from merely establishing an outer semblance of peace to creating true inner peace, Sri Sri has brought peace even to people who have never experienced it in their lives. 'Agitation and peace cannot coexist. Finding practical methods to make the mind tranquil and stress free is the only lasting approach to bring peace to society,' he says.

Using powerful breathing techniques and meditation developed by Sri Sri, his many volunteer-teachers have not only calmed the minds of powerful aggressors in different parts of the world but also provided solace and emotional strength to victims of violent conflicts.

We have seen how healing the mind helps heal the body. When the mind is in turmoil, when it is tortured and full of hatred, and when it suffers, not only unknown to itself but also radiates suffering around it, wilfully or otherwise, it translates into a diseased body and soul, diseased families and diseased nations.

'Peace begins where violence ends' is one of Sri Sri's favourite sayings, and a goal towards which he works tirelessly. In a world feeding off intolerance, insecurity, doubt and conflict, Sri Sri leads the way in extending invitations of friendship and peace. His unrelenting commitment to building bridges between estranged communities, helping people overcome the trauma of war and paving the way to mutual trust and lasting peace is truly impressive. The Art of Living has been working to promote friendly ties within and between several regions of conflict like Afghanistan, Kosovo, Pakistan, Israel, Lebanon, Nepal, India and Sri Lanka, with the aim of bringing about peace and, in turn, rapid economic growth.

In India

O India, beautiful India! Thy children sometimes go astray, but they do it with a sincerity, enthusiasm and fullness that has no match in the world! One could say that the spirit of *karma yoga* and *bhakti* pervades everyone in this country, whichever side of the fence they may seem to occupy. Today, Communism has practically died all over the world, but there still exist ardent Communists in India who follow their faith in the idea as a religion and believe firmly that it is going to make a comeback on this planet. In India one can find dedicated and selfless revolutionaries who have taken up arms because they sincerely think that no other option has been left to them by a materialistic and selfish society that does not care for its poorest and downtrodden. This is why Art of Living teachers such as Arvind B. (name changed), a man of exceptional courage and dedication, have found that these hardened criminals, who have sometimes killed more people than they can count on their fingers, have a heart of gold and are very open to Guruji's teachings.

Transforming the Minds of the Naxalites

'Naxalites are born whenever people lose faith in the political, social and economic system' goes a popular saying. Nothing can be more true. The Naxalite movement originated in the early 1960s in a West Bengal village called Naxalbari, in reaction to the oppression of poor, low caste farmers and workers by the *zamindars* or big land owners. It was brutally put down in Bengal but resurfaced in Bihar and Andhra Pradesh, where it is still prevalent today, sometimes with murderous efficiency. Naxalites emerge from the grass roots and often enjoy support from the local villagers. Nevertheless, they are ruthless, holding country courts where judgements are swift and harsh, and are masters of explosives who detonate bombs under police buses or even ministers' cars with devastating effect.

Sri Sri, along with his seva volunteers and teachers, has been working in the Naxal-infested areas of Jehanabad in Bihar since 2002. During his many visits there, Sri Sri always asks the Naxals to gift all their anger and hatred to him as *guru dakshina* and to come together in a spirit of service and celebration. Over the years, more than 1,00,000 youth from warring groups have united and vowed to give up arms and to spread the message of non-violence.

Addressing a public meeting in Bihar, Sri Sri once said, 'The Naxalites are just kids who have gone astray. They have the collective potential to do enormous good to society, provided they renounce violence and work for the common good. I consider them children who, fed up with an uncaring and insensitive society, have taken up the gun.' He added, 'They are true patriots and have the good of the common man and society at heart. It's just that the means they have chosen can only bring pain and not much else. They have tremendous energy. It only needs to be diverted towards more positive means to achieve the same ends that they seek now.'

But can spiritualism be an antidote to the poisonous influence of violence, fear and vendetta?

The answer is 'yes' for Indu Sinha, a teacher of Art of Living from Bihar. Indu, who is an ardent believer in the efficacy of spiritualism, has first-hand experience of the magic worked by the yoga, breathing techniques and meditation taught as part of the workshops. She has visited both Senari and Miyapur villages in the Naxalite affected districts of Jehanabad and Aurangabad, and gauged the psyche of the people there. Sinha says of her visit to Senari: 'I was moved by the plight of the women of Senari who suffered police brutality following the massacre in which 34 members of a particular caste were killed by Naxalites. The situation was worse than I had imagined.' When she visited Miyapur, she was horrified by the animal-like existence of the people. 'Living in my own world, I could never have guessed the sub-human existence of the villagers. The village has no road and you have to cross many water-logged areas to reach anywhere. The male members of the village are mostly dead and the villagers comprised mainly of women, and their condition was pitiable,' she says.

After this visit, she decided to do something to help them through the Vyakti Vikas Kendra. She began to work on a project to open a school and a dispensary at Senari. They are also planning a project which will provide employment to women. 'The Art of Living tries to help people by making them independent enough to solve their own problems. To begin with, we have planned a primary school and a dispensary where doctors from Jehanabad and Gaya will attend to the villagers,' she says.

Surprisingly, Indu undertook the entire journey to Senari on her own, undeterred by popular apprehensions about the law and order situation. She said that she got the strength to be on her own because of the lessons she had learnt through the Art of Living. However, she added that the reason behind her success was the support that she has received from the women of Senari.

Bihar, the cradle of knowledge and education in ancient times and home to the famed Nalanda University, has today become one of the most backward and poorest states of India. This state which was the refuge of Buddha is today one of the most violent states in India and is the heart of the Naxalite movement.

The Art of Living is working tirelessly to bring back peace and prosperity to this region through its many programmes. Through its courses, it brings back to this state its own ancient wisdom in practical forms so that those who follow the path of violence retrace their steps and come back to create an oasis of peace and togetherness.

Vijay, from Bhojpur, Bihar—who has been involved in massacres that cost the lives of over 500 people—realized, after taking part in the workshops conducted by the followers of Sri Sri, that only love can heal:

> We have been involved in multiple crimes and massacres for many years now. The whole region is gripped by interminable fear. The fight seemed endless till we went to Guruji. Now, with what we have learnt from him, we will spread our message with love, not with weapons. After meeting Guruji and experiencing the sudarshan kriya, we have realized that what we were doing was wrong. Using violence with people is not the way to solve problems or express anguish. Only love can heal. To accept people, win their hearts and be happy with oneself is the aim of love.

Many of us tend to look at problems through the prism of our own narrow thinking. We see them from our own point of view without really searching for the truth behind. This leads us to take actions that hurt others, both physically and mentally; and in turn we hurt our own selves, leading to problems both in the body and mind. Mahindar, also from Bhojpur, started to ask himself the right questions after taking the Art of Living course:

> The course made me question myself for the first time in my life. I asked myself what I was doing. Why was I killing people? What was it giving me? I realized that I was doing something utterly futile and heinous. Killing people was wrong. Accepting people with love is the right thing, is the only right way. Make people happy and be happy within oneself—that is the right thing to do.

Hare Krishna, too, has started to look at things in a broader perspective, having realized the effects of negative thinking:

> I have been a victim of negative influences all around me. I have never had the courage to question them. In fact, I was not even conscious that my way of thinking is dangerous for my own life. I did not know what peace meant. It is only here that I realized that there is nothing like cast or creed. Lust, anger, greed, attachment—all need to be removed from the system. Love is the only truth. With love, we can achieve anything. Our progress, our family's progress, our country's progress, our society's progress—all of these can happen only with love, not by threats, not by bribes. We pray for the strength to help us transform the whole society. We take a vow to bring Guruji's knowledge to each and every village in this country.

The experience of many of those who have done the sudarshan kriya has been that of developing a feeling of love and belongingness. It was the same for Ajay Kumar from Sahar. He has been so inspired that he not only gave up arms and the path of violence, but wants to go one step further and spread the love he has at last experienced:

> After coming to the Art of Living, I realized that my colleagues and I have wasted our lives in this useless war. Now we feel that we were totally wrong. When we return, we have a lot to do with what we have learnt here. The knowledge and the love we have gained can only grow with us. We will spread it across and make sure that it keeps spreading. This is the only way to rebuild what we have destroyed. This is the only way to redeem ourselves.

In the southern state of Andhra Pradesh, which has grown and prospered a great deal in the last decade, a lot of disparity in the distribution of wealth led to the spread of the Naxalite movement. Once again, the visionary Sri Sri Ravi Shankar sent his brave and dedicated volunteers into this area to bring about transformation. When one sees those Naxalites who have surrendered and have gone through the course, one is humbled by the humanity and simplicity of these men and women who share their experiences with an open heart, of the release of anguish, guilt and pain and the joy that they have now found after being introduced to the sudarshan kriya.

Ravi Naik, district leader of Naxalites in Khadri (Hyderabad) is one of those who left the path of violence to walk the path of non-violence:

> I have been leading close to 5000 people who are ready to unleash any kind of destruction in the region at my command. I have masterminded several bus and train bombings and committed over 500 murders. These facts, I thought, made me a strong and effective leader. Frustrated by economic problems, I had taken to the Naxalite movement, little realizing that I was taking the coward's way out. Guruji is the only person who has understood us. His teachings, pranayama and yoga have helped us to think with a calm mind. I have misused my leadership skills. I have misguided the people who are loyal to me. Now, we would like to join hands with Guruji to take his message to everyone.

Today he has led many youngsters involved with the Naxal movement towards the path of peace.

In a society in turmoil, it is often the women who suffer the most. They often adopt the methods and habits of men for reasons of survival and take to the path of violence, as did Amravati Shanti from Hyderabad. She had committed thirty murders and was involved in multiple bombings before she came upon the Art of Living course:

> I became a Naxalite leader owing to lack of support from the government. Disillusioned and angry, I took

to living in the forest along with a band of similarly disturbed people. We needed help. We needed guidance. But somewhere, our voices got lost in the method we adopted to put our point across. The course has taught me a new language. My life is transformed!

Bandiya Master, state general secretary of Naxalites in Andhra Pradesh, notorious for having masterminded the killings of many politicians and bombed police stations, buses and trains, has this to share on the making of a Naxalite:

Whenever people lose faith in the political, social and economic system, Naxalites are born. Naxalite movements are used as platforms to solve the problems of the people. Naxalite groups in India have multiplied over the last decade. I do not know the end of this crossfire. It will continue till the pressing problems of the people are solved. We need to be heard.

This other Naxalite leader from Hyderabad, who prefers to remain anonymous, shared why he became part of this brutal and violent group:

I would beg for a job, but nobody would give me one. I then became a Naxalite. My accomplices and I collectively worked with 2500 Naxalites. Our activities included making weapons and carrying out multiple killings and bombings in our region. We made bombs and guns in the forest and had 275 villages under our command. With what I have learnt from the Art of Living course, I look forward to going back to the forest to do agriculture. There is also the hope of getting schools in our villages and of getting exposed to different means of livelihood, which we had been unaware of till now. The course has given me a clearer perspective and I have realized that I do not need to beg. I can generate work for myself. Killing people is no solution. I have been in the wrong.

He has seen the light after participating in the workshop and is now ready to take this knowledge to others and start a new life.

Another Naxalite, who also wishes to remain anonymous, has also forsaken this violent path in order to heal himself and others through peaceful means. While the path of violence got him involved in planning killings and bombings, contact with peace within has led him back to spreading peace outwards into society.

> My shop in the city was burnt down, and I wanted justice. A mad rage filled my mind, and I took to guns. I had lost my ability to reason and think. Now I am transformed. Life is not about reacting to situations and events with a streak of bitterness or violence. It is a process which I have to go through. I have to go forward. So far I had just been stuck doing something that was utterly meaningless, attacking and indulging in a meaningless war. Now armed with this realization I will be able to influence a lot of people and stop a lot of violence. It is a change which I will share with all I can.

Creating a Sense of Trust in Kashmir

For over 2000 years, the Himalayan valley of Kashmir has been the fount of wisdom from where masterpieces of history, poetry, romance, fables and philosophy have emerged. Many of the greatest Sanskrit scholars and poets were born in this valley. Kashmir flourished under some of the greatest rulers, such as Mauryan emperor Ashoka, who is said to have founded the city of Srinagar. Under his rule, many Buddhist scholars, missionaries and intellectuals settled in the valley. Later, King Harsha, a great connoisseur of music and the arts, made his court in Srinagar a centre of learning, splendour and luxury.

At the time of independence, India and Pakistan were partitioned and Maharaja Hari Singh, then ruler of Kashmir, decided to attach his state to free and secular India. Furious, the newly-formed Pakistani government invaded Kashmir and encouraged the plunder and loot of the homes and hearths of innocent Kashmiris in general, and Hindus in particular. This conflict over territory still continues and India has fought three wars with Pakistan over land occupied illegally by them. The proxy war waged by Pakistan by arming, training and financing the Kashmiri separatists has cost the lives of over 60,000 innocents, both Hindus and Muslims. It has also resulted in Hindus fleeing the valley because of a campaign of terror against them. Today, 4,50,000 Kashmiri pandits are refugees in their own country, living in camps in Delhi and Jammu. The rich cultural heritage of this region has been destroyed as a result of the continued aggression, persecution and displacement.

The conflict in Kashmir perhaps makes it the most dangerous hotspot in South Asia. Yet, in the last five years, Sri Sri has been quietly paving the road to peace by bringing together all sections of the Kashmiri population. Sri Sri's volunteers have been organizing workshops for various sections of the Kashmiri landscape, including military personnel, militants, prison inmates, those affected by violence, etc. Art of Living volunteers ventured into the 'killing fields' of Doda and Bhadrwah at a time when these border areas were infested with camps of foreign militants who coerced the youth into militancy, often at gunpoint.

Those of us who have had the privilege of observing how Sri Sri has worked in Kashmir have been wonderstruck. I, for one, thought it was preposterous that Kashmiri terrorists would accept to do the kriya, chant *Aum* and generally undergo the course. I have been reporting on Kashmir for the past sixteen years. I have been to the Line of Control twice, been shot at by Pakistani gunners on the road to Kargil, gone with the army during night operations near Wular lake, talked to militants and interviewed separatist leaders. My impression was that these people did not want to be part of the Indian State. Yet, miracle of miracles, thanks to the grace behind the technique and the remarkable efforts of quite a few Art of Living teachers, a number of terrorists have undergone the course and been transformed for the better.

Let us begin with the remarkable story of the first teacher who ventured into Kashmir, Shyama Sondhi, and how it all started for her.

> Life was comfortable with no real worries. There was no particular prelude to my participating in the basic course. It would just be a casual course, or so I thought.
>
> Midway through the sudarshan kriya, I started feeling suffocated. So I pushed myself up to escape through the door. But as I did so, there was a ruffle of whiteness beside me and I felt the touch of three fingers on my shoulder, followed by a silent whisper: 'Don't move ... keep breathing. You will be able to do it, I am helping you.' The feel of the touch lingered on. I felt the presence of a saintly figure giving me assurance. Then I was bathed in moonlight bright as sunshine. My breathing went on in its different rhythms. I let go of myself (it just happened).
>
> Later, I heard somebody crying his heart out with such acute anguish and pain that tears sprang to my eyes. The intensity and vulnerability of that outburst was unbearable. When we were lying down after the kriya, I experienced an unusual form of sadness. An overwhelming emptiness engulfed me. When I finally opened my eyes, I found several pairs of eyes looking at me. I felt awkward at the way the other participants were taking care of me. I asked the person sitting next to me why I was being given so much attention. She told me, 'You cried a lot. Why, what is wrong?'
>
> Then the realization dawned on me that *I* had been the one crying my heart out! The entire episode was vivid in my memory but as a witness. Then I looked around for the person who had stood next to me during the kriya but I couldn't perceive anyone similar to that saintly presence in the room.

That night I slept like a newborn. Sudarshan kriya had stripped away long years of emotional blocks and tapped into my inner happiness. Physically, my immune system improved. The chronic pain in my lower back, which doctors had not been able to cure for years, vanished instantly.

When I went to attend the advanced course at Rishikesh, I had the honour of meeting Sri Sri personally for the first time (I had not even seen his photograph till then). I was stunned because he was the one who had stood next to me during the difficult moments of my first kriya, keeping his hand on my shoulder. I was equally amazed at his remark: 'So you have come!'

Doda in Jammu was at one time the hotbed of terror and separatist unrest. Many a misguided Kashmiri Muslim had gone to Pakistan from there for training in weapons and explosives and returned to spread terror and death in the once-peaceful Doda district—and Rafi was one of them. Enticed by the fiery discourses about 'Indian imperialism' and 'Kashmiri freedom' and indoctrinated at one of the many training camps inside Pakistan Occupied Kashmir, where he was taught the use of the deadly Kalashnikov and Stinger guns, he came back calling himself a jihadi and a mujaheddin (freedom fighter), although he did not even know the meaning of jehad. Before he was captured by the Indian Army, he participated in several militant activities in the valley, including a bomb attack on a CRPF convoy, in which he partially lost the use of one of his hands. After spending one year in jail, he was released and put in an Indian Army probation camp for ex-militants, where the army commander organized an Art of Living course for Rafi and his comrades. This workshop was taught by Shyama Sondhi, who says:

> The first two days, Rafi kept a certain distance. I would not say that he was hostile, but perhaps circumspect. Rafi's first sudarshan kriya saw his body go through acute stiffness, followed by frenzied shivering, only to

purge him of all the negative stress and conflict in his mind. After the kriya, he looked dazed, but more at peace with himself. During the second kriya, I could see that he went through a deep cleansing process, pain and wonderment, and finally, joy and peace mirrored on his face. The next three days, Rafi blossomed: he talked, laughed, joked, cried and finally embraced us all, sharing his relief and new-found joy of living. 'I have rediscovered what life is about,' he told me on the last morning. Today, Rafi is a responsible man who works for the betterment of his village. He is also able to make good use of his damaged hand. 'Before this,' he says, 'I had never smiled in my life.'

Another teacher who has worked hard and with great courage is Sanjay B. Who would have thought that this gentle, smiling, unprepossessing guy is actually an adventurer who goes to the most dangerous places in India! If Sanjay were to write a book one day, it would be the stuff of a thriller for sure. Here are the experiences of some of the men he has brought back to the path of peace and love. One such person, Ahmed Khalid, recounts his experiences thus:

> For the last twelve years, I had scorched myself in a self-inflicted war. I had become a militant. Life could come to an end any day. In fact, little did I realize that I was destroying myself with every passing day. I was fighting for something, but it eluded me because it was not love, it was not peace. Thank god it eluded me! This year, everything changed. A friend of mine got me to do the course, after which I had the opportunity to meet Guruji in person. For thirteen years, I had not seen my mother. Guruji told me that he would send me home. Yes, now I am home, not just with my mother, but with a family that is bigger and filled with more love than I ever imagined. Guruji is the head of this family. He is with me always.

Then there is Khalid, from Srinagar, who has forsaken the path of violence after doing the course:

> There is not a single individual here who hasn't been a victim of wrongdoing. We have propagated ravages that created more problems than solutions. After the course, I was able to see my situation, my surroundings and my objective in an entirely different light. I realized that I had been supporting something wrong. Now, taking the path shown by Guruji, my companions and I strongly feel that we will be able to solve the issues we feel strongly about.

Mohamed Shafi sums it up:

> Guruji's visit to Kashmir has been the most effective and positive catalyst for the restoration of peace in the valley. He has touched us in a way nobody has. We have all experienced a sea change in our beliefs. Not too many people in Kashmir knew about the Art of Living. Probably that is why militancy could take root here.

During his visits to Kashmir, Sri Sri not only touched the lives of the militants but also arranged meetings with the leaders of the All Parties Hurriyat Conference and representatives of the Kashmiri pandits. These two opposing groups came face to face with each other for the first time since the conflict began.

The work being done by the Art of Living in the valley has brought those who left the path of peace back into the fold and has built bridges between the separatists and those they oppose. As Shabbir, a reformed militant, puts it, 'Just as an iron rod bends with the power of heat, so too my life has taken a turn for the better. Guruji has melted my rigidity and moulded me into somebody who is no more afraid to listen, understand and love.'

Many of those who joined militancy groups were misguided youth, frustrated by the prevailing unrest and in desperate search of a goal in life. However they discovered themselves and found peace after they started performing pranayama and sudarshan kriya. As Sajjat Hussein says:

> It is easy to want happiness but difficult to understand that we can have it very easily if we truly want it. After doing the course, everything became simple for me. Everything was within me, within my reach. I experienced a joy and a happiness which I had been unaware of till then. I felt closer to Allah, and found another source of inspiration and strength to keep me going—Guruji. His grace has truly healed me.

Says Wasim Ahmed from Anantnag, who has graduated from being a terrorist to a youth leader:

> The Youth Leadership Training programme has given me immense strength, self-belief and compassion. I used to while away my time in futile activities, not pausing to reflect on where I was actually headed. Now I realize that life is precious and take full responsibility for my actions and my life.

Sri Sri has also started an orphanage for over 30,000 young victims of militancy who were likely to become easy targets for recruitment into militant groups. The orphanage not only provides shelter but also imparts multicultural, multiethnic education.

Elsewhere

Today the Art of Living is slowly but steadily making a difference in the world of Islam—not by trying to convert or take away Muslims from their religion, but by giving those misguided by false notions of their religion a tool that they can use to become better Muslims, and indeed better human beings who are capable of accepting diversity and recognizing the fact that other worlds and other creeds that are worthy of their respect exist too. As Sri Sri has often stressed, spirituality is beyond religion and has the power to unite people from all backgrounds.

Iraq

Iraq has had to face the wrath of the world's superpowers in recent times and the consequences manifest themselves till date, not only in the form of civil violence, economic breakdown and infrastructural shortages, but more significantly, in the form of the devastated morale of its people. Sri Sri turned his attention towards Iraq soon after the attack in September 2003 by sending many volunteers to teach the Art of Living programmes there. As Ali, a forty-four-year-old electrical engineer with a government railway company in Iraq, who completed the Art of Living course, recalls:

> We lived in constant fear of death. Indeed, death could come from any direction. One day, I met a friend at the local market and stopped to exchange pleasantries with him when we heard a huge explosion. The glass shattered all around us. We flung ourselves on the ground. Later, we found many cars completely demolished. My car's doors had been flung away, the tyres had burst. Had I not stopped to talk to my friend, I would have died. Allah's mercy is infinite.
>
> I was a very angry, stressed person before. The course made me feel much more at peace with myself. My family, including my wife and six children, saw such a difference in me that they said, 'If this course has made you so happy, do another one!'

Mawahib Al Shaibani, an Arab Art of Living teacher from the UAE who was part of the first team of volunteers that reached Iraq in September 2003, explained how their programmes were positioned as a tool to help people combat war stress rather than as any kind of religion or sect. In fact, another Art of Living volunteer, Mulki, said that several of the participants told him that their *namaaz* had become more meaningful after they did the workshops.

In many Islamic countries, women have been secluded and have often had to bear the brunt of the conflict raging in their countries. The breathing and meditation techniques taught at the programmes gave many locals relief from depression, anxiety, blood pressure, migraines and psychosomatic disorders. People who had previously been unable to sleep because of constant nightmares reported peaceful sleep. In Ballad, Iraq, close to where Saddam Hussein was eventually captured, the programmes were conducted entirely in burqa.

Says Mawahib about Iraqi women joining Art of Living courses:

> After thirty-five years of war, they (the Iraqis) could relax and feel free for the first time with us. Women, especially, had not been encouraged to look outside the Koran for anything. They felt that all that we had to say was very new, but at the same time they could relate to it very easily, because it's very practical. Islam literally means living in peace, only that they had never experienced it before.

'Thinking about the past is futile,' said Mulook, a course participant, 'Meditation keeps me confident and alive.'

Shortly after doing his first Art of Living course, Ali helped Dr Santosh organize another course and eventually became his interpreter. Ali was also subsequently part of a delegation from Iraq to India for advanced training in the Art of Living. He and his companions, Amman, Mulook and Wafaa, arrived in Mumbai and completed several courses, each revealing in a new way the immense power of this knowledge to effect an inner transformation. He said, 'In Arabic, the word "habibi" means love. I had heard that word hundreds of times in my life but when Guruji hugged me and said, "habibi," the word entered my heart directly, like an arrow. For the first time, I understood the true meaning of the word.'

On being asked what he would do when he returns to Iraq after finishing his teachers' training course part II, Ali replied, 'Teach, of course! My family and friends ... and help my country. We Iraqis have gone through years of stress, tension and trauma, and are in great need of techniques like the Art of Living. After all, breath has no religion!'

Each participant's tryst with the Art of Living was a powerful and life-changing one.

'I came to the ashram for the first time in 2006 and that was the most beautiful month of my life. The Art of Living has taught me how to take care of myself as well as others. We are so unaware of the importance of our own breath and how it can help us reach a stage where there is absolute clarity and focus,' says Mariam, a member of the Iraqi Parliament and an ex-advisor to the Iraqi prime minister.

It was sheer curiosity about Sri Sri Ravi Shankar's 'Health through Breath' programme that attracted her to the Art of Living. Today, she is involved in it—hook, line and sinker. After completing the introductory programme, she followed it up with advanced courses and the teacher's training programme.

'I was so fired up by the experience and Sri Sri's vision of a violence-free and stress-free world that I started teaching the Art of Living programme to top politicians in Iraq, and it was a huge success,' she recalls.

Her story moved Iraqi Prime Minister Nouri al-Maliki so much that he invited Sri Sri to visit Iraq in 2007.

On 22 May, Sri Sri Ravi Shankar arrived in Baghdad. This was the first time that an Indian spiritual leader was invited as a peace ambassador to the conflict-ravaged country by the Government of Iraq itself. Welcoming Sri Sri to Iraq, the prime minister said, 'There are big powers that have might, but they are unable to unite the hearts and minds of people. This work can only be done by a spiritual leader.'

During the visit, Sri Sri held discussions on restoring peace in Iraq with the prime minister and also addressed a public gathering attended by several political leaders belonging to Sunni, Shia and Kurdish parties. According to Sri Sri, 'There is anger and hatred all over Iraq. Iraqis need to learn how to manage anger and reconcile with the present. This requires a shift in the mind and a change of heart. That's where spirituality has a big role to play. We are working to facilitate this process.'

Sri Sri, in his continuing efforts to bring peace to this war-torn country, met many Iraqi tribal and political leaders in Baghdad in an effort to bring the Shia and Sunni communities—which have been fighting against each other—closer and to facilitate mending fences between the two. His foundation was working towards establishing harmony among the warring factions. 'We are already doing it. If you see in our centres, we have brought the communities together. There are Sunnis and Shias, and then there are Kurdish people in the north. So, the effort to unify them has begun from the very first day,' he said.

The Art of Living has been working under trying circumstances to help Iraqis overcome the deep trauma inflicted by the long-drawn warfare and the prevailing uncertainty. Its volunteers have been conducting trauma relief workshops in various parts of Iraq, especially in Baghdad, providing not only breathing and meditation exercises but also medicines and clothes to the Iraqi populace. Even during the times when most NGOs were compelled to evacuate their volunteers from Iraq in the wake of heightened unrest and kidnapping, the Art of Living volunteers stayed put.

Moved by the effective intervention, several Iraqis have completed special training courses to impart the Art of Living techniques to the Iraqi people. In 2006, a batch of forty-three, mostly women, graduated as Art of Living teachers. So far, 5000 Iraqis have undergone the Art of Living trauma relief workshops apart from attending the Ayurvedic training camps.

The foundation has also initiated a women's empowerment project under which local women are given vocational training in tailoring and computer skills. Over 500 women have benefited from this programme. Says Mawahib:

> Some of them are widows while some have lost their family members. There is not a single family which has not lost its people. They have suffered due to the war and now they have hope, because we have given them hope. We are teaching them computers, tailoring and are also giving them trauma relief. Many Iraqis have benefited in a big way from the initiatives of the Art of Living. They got relief from depression, anxiety, blood pressure, migraine and other psychosomatic disorders resulting from war-related stress, thanks to the breathing techniques taught by our volunteers.

They have been touched by the love, support and friendship extended to them by volunteers of Art of Living who risked their own lives to teach them stress-relieving techniques and spread the message of love. As thirty-two-year-old Iraqi, Ahmed Hinoon, puts it:

> I felt really relaxed after doing the breathing exercises. This programme has changed my life. After so many years, I am able to control my mind. I am now ready to face the challenges of life. With endless killings, bombs and war, life in Iraq is very stressful. After doing the course, we see a new ray of hope.

Concurs Ramia Sagban from Baghdad: 'It is a wonderful programme. We didn't know what the Art of Living was, but after coming here we are learning a lot about our body, mind and soul and also learning to handle our emotions.'

In a rare example of how love moves the world and comes full circle, two separate groups of Iraqis and Pakistanis recently visited the ashram in Bangalore. Amar Al Shemmary explained why he and three other Iraqis had come all the way to Bangalore: 'While there are three Indians who are hostages of fear in Iraq, we are four hostages of love in India!'

In Harmony

Musicians from all over south India perform to celebrate twenty-five years of the Art of Living in 2006 at Jakkur Airfield, Bangalore, India

Spreading the Joy

Men and women being trained to carry the teachings of Sri Sri Ravi Shankar to the world—teachers' training course under way at the Art of Living International Centre, Bangalore, India

Sri Sri with the first batch of 'Yuvacharyas' or youth leaders in 1990 at the Art of Living International Centre

Students of the Heritage School at the Art of Living International Centre

Learning a Way of Life

The first rural school established by Sri Sri in 1981 in Bangalore, India

Art of Living course participants in Germany roaring like lions to get rid of their inhibitions

Participants of the Youth Empowerment Seminar course in Karachi, Pakistan

Participants of the Art of Living course in Kabul, Afghanistan

Women taking part in an Art of Living course in war-torn Kosovo

Youngsters at the All Round Training in Excellence (ART Excel) summer camp in Chechnya, Russia

Nav Chetna Shibir or Breath-Water-Sound workshop under way in Congo

Street children in Harare, Zimbabwe, doing yoga as part of an Art of Living course

The Calm After the Storm

Participants at a Youth Empowerment Seminar course in Beslan School, Russia

Residents meditating in Union Square park, New York City, to calm their minds in the aftermath of the 9/11 attacks

Sri Sri visits the survivors of Hurricane Katrina as a guest of the city of Austin in Texas, USA

Tsunami survivors in Sri Lanka with the fishing nets donated by the International Association for Human Values, a sister concern of the Art of Living Foundation, to help restore their livelihood

A Happy Harvest

Beneficiaries of the 5H programme that focusses on 'health, hygiene, homes, human values and harmony in diversity' in Bangalore, India

Training being imparted to women at Vista, a vocational centre for rural women in Bangalore, India

 A prison inmate making paper bags during the SRIJAN (Social Rehabilitation of Inmates in Jail and Aiding the Needy) programme in Tihar Jail, New Delhi, India

Uniform Calm

Indian Army participants after an Art of Living course in Kargil, India

The Moods of the Guru

Sri Sri being welcomed at the Ajmer Sharif dargah in Rajasthan, India

Sri Sri singing a bhajan at a satsang in New Delhi, India

The guru cooks for course participants in Bad Antogast, Germany

The tech-savvy guru with his laptop on board a plane in Europe

Sri Sri speaks to a captive audience at Warwick University, UK

Sri Sri visiting the flood-ravaged state of Bihar in India

In the Company of Truth

Thousands gather for satsang at the Vishalakshi Mantap at the Art of Living International Centre

I met a radiant Iraqi woman named Wafaa who had come to India only because of Sri Sri Ravi Shankar's Art of Living course, and whose journey to India had been filled with grace and adventure. At a time when passports were hardly ever issued in Iraq, she had managed to get one within a few days. Almost immediately thereafter, she drove down to Jordan to catch a Royal Jordanian flight to Mumbai. This was a person who had not travelled even within Iraq by herself, let alone out of it! 'But,' she said, 'I did not feel alone. Everyone became like my family. By the grace of Allah, they even put me in first class.'

In Mumbai, to her dismay, there was no one from the Art of Living to meet her. Many phone calls later, Wafaa learnt that the Art of Living as well as her fellow Iraqis (who had already arrived in Mumbai) had not received her message with her flight details! 'But all is well that ends well,' says Wafaa. 'We all met up and laughed and rejoiced together at being finally here in India. Looking at life from a bigger perspective, what could have been a very frustrating experience became a joke.'

When I asked Wafaa how she became interested in Art of Living in the first place, she said:

> One day my brother-in-law, who works in the Iraqi Ministry of Electricity, came home and said, 'All is not lost! There is still humanity in this world. Indian volunteers have come from an organization called The Art of Living to help us. They say that the breathing technique they teach can really help heal the stress, trauma and grief that we have been suffering.' As we ate our lunch, I thought to myself, 'Who is this man who can inspire volunteers to come to war-torn Iraq at a time when we Iraqis are afraid to move around our own cities?'
>
> Because I had read articles and seen programmes on TV about breathing techniques in India, China and Japan that can help healing, I decided I wanted to do the course offered by the Art of Living volunteers. I found out from my brother-in-law that Dr Sampath, the

Art of Living teacher, was conducting another course. I immediately took a week's leave from my office with the mayor of Baghdad and enrolled myself in the course.

When we did the sudarshan kriya, something happened ... like a dream. I can't explain it. During the sudarshan kriya, I felt great pain in my chest area; my eye and the corner of my lip started twitching a lot. I felt very afraid. I stopped following the breathing, but Dr Sampath came and urged me to continue. After the sudarshan kriya, all the pain went away.

The meditation sessions were like magic, especially the expanding one. We were sitting on chairs, not on cushions like here in the ashram. My arms were resting on the arms of the chair. Suddenly, I felt as if I was nothing! Nothing at all! I could not feel anything touching the chair. I did not know what it was but felt as if I was nothing. So light!

The last day, we had a lot of fun. We did something different that we had never done before. All twenty-five of us in the course had been complete strangers to each other on the first day of the course. But on that last day we felt like one family. We shared food and had a sense of belongingness. That was when I wondered, more than ever, 'Who is this man who can inspire and create courses like this?'

Once I had learnt this amazing technique, I wanted to spread it in the world. Air is a gift from God. We need to know how to use it correctly. The techniques taught by the Art of Living are the perfect way to use air and breath.

And I have also now discovered the living inspiration who encourages people to go out without fear into conflict situations like Iraq—Guruji. I have never met a man like him before. Even though we are of the same age, he is like a father to me.

In April 2005, Wafaa became an Art of Living teacher and returned to Iraq with what she called 'the biggest gift of all'—the Art of Living course to help the people of her country.

During Sri Sri's visit to Iraq, many Iraqi leaders agreed that what was most needed in the world today is non-violence and reconciliation. According to Guruji, 'This can only happen when the mind is relieved of stress and the emotions are softened and refined. This state cannot be achieved by force or violence. Only through meditation and breathing techniques can we attain this, as has been demonstrated around the world.'

Once again, on 11 August 2009, we saw a group of thirty-five-odd people from various Islamic nations seeking a different kind of IT in India's information technology capital, Bangalore. They have come all the way to create a programme of 'inner Transformation'—for themselves and for the people back home.

The members of the motley group, including nationals from Morocco, Palestine, Iraq and Pakistan, were there to undergo the teachers' training programme at the Art of Living International Centre, to become Art of Living instructors.

Yusuf Majid, a fifty-year-old from Lebanon shares his experiences with us:

> The war and the ongoing violence took me to a point where I felt that I will collapse any minute. I often had suicidal thoughts. I had become heartless; no relationship mattered to me. Then I was introduced to the Art of Living by a friend in 2000. Thanks to it, I feel more optimistic, balanced and ready for anything in life. It has made me go deeper into my faith and now I feel safe and beautiful from within. Now I want to take this skill of managing life to my people; make them experience what I did and give them a chance to bring about this beautiful change, in their own lives and that of others.

Yusuf isn't alone. Interestingly, all the participants from the Middle East believe that the inner transformation they are experiencing can be a remedy for many of the maladies that ail the world. 'Only when I am in harmony will I be able to create harmony around myself. The Art of Living has helped me to experientially understand the feeling of harmony. Sri Sri has made us understand that there is no "You" and "Me". It is only "We" and "Us",' says Farida.

'We need more people who understand this and come together to work towards creating a harmonious society. Now, I aim to reach out to the thousands who are in dire need of this wisdom,' she adds.

In addition to preparing themselves for what they term a 'huge responsibility to humanity', these Art of Living participants are also making the most of their stay in the ashram and learning about India and its people and culture through the different activities of the ashram. 'I like the atmosphere and the energy of this place. There are people from diverse backgrounds, yet there is a spirit of belongingness and so much positivity,' says Farida. 'I gel well with everyone. It is like one big family for me,' she explains.

'I just love this place. It is my home. This experience has been so refreshing and rejuvenating. *Inshallah*, we will definitely come back with more people soon,' promises Yusuf. 'For, this is IT,' he adds with a twinkle in his eye.

Drive for Peace in West Asia: Israel and Palestine

Israel has a unique place in history as it is the cradle of three major religions of the world. Ironically, it is history itself, or more accurately, different perceptions of history, that have impacted the Arab-Israeli conflict most. Varying accounts and interpretations of history are used alternately to justify claims and to negate them, to vilify the enemy and to glorify 'our own side'. Sri Sri often points out that more wars have been fought on this planet in the name of religion than all else. The Art of Living is effective in such situations because it brings values like love, brotherhood and peace to life, not as an obligation or an injunction, but as an undeniable experience. In Jerusalem, it has brought together secular and religious Jews, Israeli Arabs and Palestinians. The Israeli-Palestinian conflict has brought suffering to many people on both sides. People long for true peace that will bring an end to the suffering. Along with the experience of inner peace and renewal of energy, the participants are amazed to feel the harmony and love that has blossomed among the participants in such a short span of time. The Art of Living in Israel is working to bring about harmony in diversity.

When Art of Living teacher Dafna Paz goes to teach a course in Sderot, a small town along the separation fence bordering Gaza, in the southern part of Israel, family and friends ask her if she is not afraid of the missile attacks which strike at unexpected times of the night and day. Her answer? A smile and a shake of the head, indicating a 'no'. She is confident that with Guruji's grace, everything will happen for the best in all situations.

On the day of the planned Art of Living part I course in Sderot, it was raining heavily (a most unusual event in the dry and rainless season) and missiles were being fired from across the border. As Dafna arrived at the venue, only four out of the fifteen people registered for the course had turned up. She called up each missing participant and enquired as to why they were not present. Rain and fear of the missile attacks had kept some people at home. Dafna, who drives two hours from her home in Tel Aviv to Sderot and back, in rain or shine, night or day, with or without missiles, convinced a couple of people to arrive in any case. The course started with eight people and lots of trepidation.

The second day of the course began amid the blaring sirens of ambulances and missiles exploding in the town. It turned out that one missile had landed near the homes of two course participants and they had hesitated to come until one of the women said, 'Well, it has already fallen. We might as well go to the course, but let's leave early; we will go only for an hour.' Suddenly, during the sudarshan kriya, the room and windows of the venue shook due to the explosion of two missiles. The participants continued with the kriya even as a woman asked, without opening her eyes, 'Was that a missile?' and Dafna answered in a reassuring voice, 'Yes, go on with the kriya,' which she did.

After performing the kriya, it was so peaceful inside the room that nobody stirred. Even the two women who had planned to leave early stayed for the whole session with no trepidation.

The intense and urgent need to be salvaged from the malady of war and violence can be readily felt in areas that have long been suffering from them. To address this need, courses are conducted all over Israel, with an aspiration of 'breath for peace'. The most striking positive results have been felt along the separation fence, where people on both sides of the border live with intense daily stress. Advanced meditation courses are held several times a year, inviting participants to dive into an inner place within, so deep and unshakeably still that even a crashing missile does not cause a ripple.

Many programmes have been conducted along the separation fence between the Israeli and the Palestinian territories. Art of Living volunteers work in places along the Gaza strip, and along the border in Jerusalem and Ramallah. On both sides of the border, people have been using the powerful breathing techniques to eliminate stress, fear and anxiety. Many of these people live under constant threat to their lives, so it's not surprising that many of them develop post-traumatic syndromes of extreme stress, anxiety and sleeping disorders. After the course, most experience deep relief and feel able to cope with the stressful situation they are living in. The Art of Living programmes have helped people feel more connected, and shown them that they share a mutual interest for peace.

As part of the continuing process of Art of Living Israel's motto 'breath for peace', ART Excel courses for children are conducted in Arab villages in Israel.

In August last year, Dafna Paz, who is an ART Excel teacher as well, was invited to do a course in the Israeli Arab village of Ararah, in the northern part of Israel, around the Galilee area. The organizer, an Israeli Arab peace and educational activist named Wagih Sidawi, was in charge of translating from Hebrew to Arabic for the group of twelve kids present, aged nine to thirteen. But due to his busy work schedule, he was not always available, and Dafna found herself communicating with the kids without words, more often than not, and with lots of laughter. Somehow they all understood each other very well and the course went on smoothly. The participants, especially the girls, all from families embedded in traditional Arab culture, and not as westernized as their Israeli–Jewish counterparts, felt the direct influence of the course in their everyday life. An older girl testified that the course helped her to communicate better with her family. By the end of the course, Dafna could see that the kids were more open, confident and more at ease.

Many courses have since then been conducted in the Israeli–Arab sector and have been well received.

During the war with Lebanon, Art of Living provided materials and trauma relief courses in the city of Haifa close to the northern border of Israel. The volunteers took care of those residents who could not leave the city or had to stay in underground bomb shelters by delivering water, cooked meals, fresh produce and other basic necessities. The volunteers came to play and work with the children to reduce their fear and anxiety. The programmes were made available to both the Jewish and Arab populations. Participants in the programme reported experiencing calmness and relief from anxiety and the trauma of war.

Kindling a Desire for Peace in Afghanistan

Over two decades of war and strife have almost completely ruined Afghanistan. Anyone would imagine that a place and its people who have been through so much would become totally disoriented and lose all sense of right and wrong. Disoriented they may be, but their ancient spiritual heritage has nurtured them through bad times.

'The most surprising thing that I found in Afghanistan was that in spite of the long years of war and hardship, the people there have not lost their warmth. They are very pleasant and hospitable. Their resilience is amazing,' says Ann Godwin, a post-trauma stress disorder treatment specialist, who is now a full-time volunteer with the Art of Living Foundation and the IAHV, working on its 5H programme in Afghanistan.

I met Ann when she was visiting the ashram in Bangalore along with a few Afghan women for the women's conference. She was very enthusiastic about her experience in this region. So devoid of all the material comforts that she has been used to, yet there was a glow about her and her love for the Afghans was apparent during our conversation.

I wanted to understand how receptive the people of Afghanistan had been to the techniques taught, given that Afghan society is seen as extremely conservative. I asked Ann if she had faced any problems in trying to convince them.

'Afghans are very warm and open in many ways. Also, they know they don't feel good. When I talked to them about my experience as a specialist and having seen these techniques work in places such as Kosovo (I showed them pictures of courses conducted in Kosovo, course participants, and so on), where we had worked with the Muslim population, they agreed that they wanted help and were very appreciative of the fact that we had come from distant places to provide them help and succour. They have a lot of respect for that,' replied Ann and went on to share her most memorable experience:

> We taught the ART Excel programme at this home which housed orphans and abandoned children. In spite of all the suffering that these boys had been through, there was a lot of joy and willingness to come out of the inhibitions accumulated from having to face hostile and sometimes life-threatening circumstances regularly. The course gave them a chance to not be afraid of looking like a fool. They were doing all sorts of funny things,

and then all of us started singing. It is not really in their culture to sing and play music. But they started singing and dancing. Then the adult cook, who was not part of the course, came in and spontaneously started dancing. It was a heart-warming experience. I am very fortunate to have been able to go there with these techniques and help the people. Such sessions are even more fulfilling because of the intense experiences that the Afghans have had, and the way they respond to these techniques, because of which one immediately notices the changes one has been able to bring about in their attitude.

Building Bridges with Pakistan

It is a well-worn truism that there is a deep-seated mistrust of each other between the people of India and Pakistan despite the fact that they are very similar in their looks, culture, habits and language.

In an attempt to thaw the relations between India and Pakistan, Sri Sri undertook a historic four-day peace mission to Pakistan in July 2004, becoming the first spiritual leader ever to be welcomed there. During his visit, Sri Sri met with political, business and religious leaders and social activists in Karachi and Islamabad in an effort to build mutual trust for lasting peace. The people of Pakistan responded very well to his call for peace and harmony.

'Sri Sri Ravi Shankar's recent visit to Pakistan has touched the hearts of many Pakistanis and now they want to experience more of India and Guruji in particular,' says Naeem Zamindar, an Art of Living teacher from Pakistan.

'This is a very encouraging sign for promoting peace and better understanding between the two countries. In the near future, we will see a lot more Pakistanis here,' added Naeem, who recently quit his top job with Intel Capital, USA, to spearhead Art of Living's activities in Pakistan.

'We have come here inspired by Sri Sri's message of love and this trip has provided us a new understanding of India and its culture. We really feel at home,' said Sanniya from Islamabad. 'We will go back to Pakistan and work to achieve Sri Sri's vision of a stress-free world, and spread his message of love and peace,' she added.

Sri Sri feels that India and Pakistan are the two oldest civilizations in the world and probably among the youngest countries in the world with the median age of Indians at 24.9 years and that of Pakistanis at 19.8 years. 'That's a strong enough reason,' he says, 'to demonstrate that it's the youth of both the nations who will play a great role in opening up channels of communication and understanding, thus dispelling the thick clouds of suspicion, bitterness and war.'

As part of the continuing endeavour to spread Sri Sri's message of peace and goodwill to Pakistan, the directors of WAYE (World Alliance for Youth Empowerment), the youth body of the Art of Living Foundation, Dinesh Ghodke and Khurshed Batliwala visited Pakistan to bring about a greater understanding among the youth of the two countries. Over 100 Pakistani youth in the age group of eighteen to twenty-five years underwent a week-long programme at the Indus School of Arts and Architecture, Karachi, an initiative aimed at creating better channels of understanding and communication between the two countries, breaking prejudices and bringing people together through social service, culture, arts and sports.

Recalling the trip, Dinesh says, 'They all agreed that along with food, fashion, music and technology, wisdom too needs to be globalized. The youth have a major role in strengthening the roots and broadening the vision of a nation.'

And what better sign than such cross-border engagements that give rise to the hope that spirituality is all set to fill the missing links in the effort to establish better ties between India and Pakistan!

Pushing for Peace in Sri Lanka

Another neighbour of India in conflict is Sri Lanka. For more than two decades, Tamil separatists have been waging a bitter battle against the Sinhalese majority for a homeland in the north of this once heavenly island, which has cost the lives of more than 70,000 people.

Sri Sri has been actively involved in peace negotiations in Sri Lanka. In early 2005, he sent emissaries to negotiate with the Sri Lankan president and Tamil leaders. In June 2005, Opposition leader Ranil Wickramasinghe visited the Art of Living International Centre in Bangalore and held discussions with Sri Sri. At a time of escalating tension, on the request of the Sri Lankan president, Sri Sri sent experts to conduct special programmes for decision makers, the president and army personnel, and also for the youth in north-east Sri Lanka.

Invited to Sri Lanka in September 2006 by Opposition leader and former Prime Minister Ranil Wickremesinghe and current President Mahinda Rajapakse, he ventured to Kilinochchi for peace talks with LTTE leaders (the Liberation Tigers of Tamil Eelam). His visit came at a time of tremendous civil unrest. However, his interactions with the locals as well as the country's top brass have been instrumental in changing mindsets. He remains actively involved in brokering peace between the government and the LTTE, the main (and most deadly) separatist group.

Sri Sri met 80,000 Sri Lankans, including the Sinhalese, the Tamil, political leaders, Buddhist monks, and diplomats to discuss peace. As a result of these talks and ongoing Art of Living programmes, hundreds of Tamil youth in Jaffna have given up violence and are working with volunteers to bring relief to the people of northeastern Sri Lanka, who have been traumatized by more than two decades of ethnic violence. He has also been responsible for the formation of a committee for peace comprising Hindu and Buddhist leaders, including the Dalai Lama, to take the peace agenda forward.

During his visit to Jaffna, the Art of Living centre there received a few threatening calls asking to cancel the satsang programme of Sri Sri scheduled for the evening as an LTTE leader had been shot dead in Trincomali just a few hours before. Organizers were told that they would have to take full responsibility if any untoward incident happened during the programme. Peaceful and calm as usual, Sri Sri went ahead with the satsang, where he led thousands into a deep meditation. After the twenty-minute meditation, many shared that they had never experienced such peace and joy in their life.

A delegation of the members of parliament from Sri Lanka expressed confidence that Sri Sri's participation would take the peace process forward in spite of setbacks at the Geneva peace talks. They were taking part in a special Art of Living programme called 'Peace and Reconciliation' at the International Centre in Bangalore.

'The programme has renewed our conviction to work for peace. Peace has to begin from within. We feel after coming [to Bangalore] that our vision has become broader, and we realize the value of peace, love, compassion, and non-violence. This will make us better equipped to face the challenges we face as leaders in our country,' said Dr Jayalath Jayawardana, head of United National Party (UNP) relief and humanitarian rights committee, Sri Lanka.

In April 2008, the IAHV organized a historic conference on South Asian conflicts in Oslo, Norway, which focussed on the internal armed conflicts in South Asian nations, particularly Sri Lanka. It was attended by both pro-LTTE leaders, as well as by Sinhalese monks whom Sri Sri managed to bring together. Norway's special envoy for the peace process in Sri Lanka, Jon Hanssen-Bauer; members of European Parliament, Erika Mann and Nirj Deva; and Aud Kvalbein, the deputy mayor of Oslo were some of the prominent European speakers at the symposium. The conference was a great success.

At the peak of the conflict, when the government sent its army to clear Jaffna and the areas under the LTTE's control in

April–May 2009, the government had moved the civilian Tamil residents trapped in these areas to safety, into various camps. Sri Sri visited the Internally Displaced People (IDP) welfare centres in Vavuniya, Sri Lanka on 21 April. He appreciated the selfless service of the army personnel in the welfare centres and the help that they extended to the Art of Living to distribute clothes, medicine, food and other relief materials in the camps.

During his visit, he also met President Mahinda Rajapakse and conveyed the desire of the Tamils to return to their homes soon. 'The untold suffering of the Tamils will make any heart bleed. A place that had never seen beggars has to now beg for water, food, clothes and for life itself,' he said. He also appealed to the president to avoid the long stay of Tamils in the IDP camps. 'Pregnant women, the elderly, the rich, the poor ... they are all languishing in these camps,' he said. Sri Sri was assured by the president regarding the safety of these civilians in the camps and that the civilians would be re-settled in their home towns after the areas had been de-mined.

Sri Sri concluded his three-day peace mission to Sri Lanka assuring the displaced Tamils that they would return in peace to their homes very soon. 'A new dawn is in the offing. Stay calm and peaceful. The Art of Living Foundation and I are right with you in your hour of need,' he said after visiting the camp.

Sri Sri's visit gave the people an opportunity to give vent to their suppressed emotions and also assured them that they were cared for.

Taming Ethnic Hatred in Kosovo

'We thank Kosovo for sending Mother Teresa to India. India will reciprocate by bringing the benefits of yoga and its ancient spiritual knowledge, which is much needed in Kosovo today,' Sri Sri Ravi Shankar said on a two day visit to Kosovo in September 2007.

The Kosovo area of the Balkans has been an embattled area through history for most of the last 2000 years. The inability of ethnic Serbs and Albanians to coexist, and the resultant insecurities were the overriding reasons for conflict. The last decade of the previous millennium however witnessed unprecedented ethnic cleansing and rebellion. Sri Sri calls 'war' the 'worst act of reason' and it's not difficult to see why.

The Kosovo conflict ended in June 1999 with the withdrawal of Serbian troops and the initiation of the United Nations' peacekeeping effort in Kosovo. Violence briefly reared its head once again in March 2004. Fortunately, it was quickly brought under control, although Kosovo's unilateral declaration of independence has again brought tension in the region.

According to statistics made available by the Association of Disabled Kosovo Liberation Army Veterans and LDK Information Centre, there are 2634 disabled Kosovo Liberation Army veterans, 13,000 people were killed during the war, 3500 persons disappeared, 34,000 women were raped and tortured, and the number of people who were imprisoned or who went through police questioning is 7,00,000.

A Harvard medical group assessed the effects of war in Kosovo and found that around 80 per cent of the people there suffer from post traumatic stress disorder or PTSD. PTSD affects people who have witnessed, or have been involved in life-threatening events such as war, rape or road accidents. The symptoms include flashbacks, nightmares, depression and heightened psychological arousal. Brain scanning has revealed differences in the ways that traumatized and healthy brains respond to the world. Current medical research is bringing evidence using sophisticated means such as CAT scans and MRIs, and we are finding that individuals with PTSD symptomatology have significant difficulties with central nervous system functioning following the impact of trauma.

In the aftermath of armed conflict, there was a need to work with the survivors to promote healing. The Art of Living activity began immediately after the cessation of hostilities in Drenice, an area badly hit by civilian massacres and violence. Teachers and volunteers from the foundation started stress-elimination workshops with the Kosovo Liberation Army (KLA). Many of its members were suffering from symptoms of PTSD and physical wounds. With breath-enhancing tools to reconcile with the past, mental healing took place quickly in case of most beneficiaries. The Art of Living breathing techniques are not only found to be more effective in dealing with these symptoms, but once taught, these techniques keep helping students by renewing and re-invigorating their systems and thereby improving their overall health whenever they practise them.

Soon Art of Living was conducting courses for every section of society, healing scars and giving tools by which the future could be lived fully and happily. The Art of Living also worked in collaboration with several agencies in Kosovo to restore and strengthen the infrastructure of the province.

Now the Art of Living—with such teachers as Snjezana Nivesic (director of the Art of Living programme for Kosovo and Albania) and Sanja Kordic, both graduates of Zagreb University—teaches full-time in Croatia, Bosnia, Kosovo, Serbia and Macedonia, which are some of the most volatile places in Europe today. They have been doing wonderful pioneering work there. Says Snjezana, 'I have been working with trauma victims in the war-torn Balkans, especially Kosovo, since the early post-war days. Many of those who took the Art of Living course were terribly traumatized, but the courses helped them move beyond the trauma and regain their centre.'

Again, in Snjezana's own words:

> We started spreading Guruji's knowledge in Kosovo immediately after the war. It was difficult, yet wonderful work and one would often have to stick Art of Living posters on tanks. Kosovo is inhabited by orthodox Muslims who are closed to new knowledge, and at the same time are wonderful, hospitable, and full of gratefulness and respect for this knowledge as soon as they open up.

Amongst Snjezana's students, here is an exceptional testimony by someone who not only experienced the hell of war and the torture of prison, but whose body had also been wrecked by the mental anguish he had to live through. Narrates Vehbi Rafun, former director of the Association of Disabled KLA Veterans:

I lost my parents when I was two. As an orphan, I was sent to military school. In 1974, when I was a teenager, I realized that the Albanians in Kosovo were treated as second-rate citizens. Kosovo was isolated at that time and the communist regime did not allow freedom of speech. Due to my public speeches and participation in demonstrations, I was sentenced to nine years in prison.

As a political prisoner, my life turned to hell. I was threatened, humiliated, beaten, burnt with hot objects, given electric shocks, questioned all night and deprived of sleep and food. Each time I lost consciousness, they would splash cold water in my face and continue torturing me.

I served in the KLA from 1994 to 1999 and was wounded in the left leg and spine. This wound left me with a permanent physical disability. I was subsequently founder and director of the Association for Disabled Kosovo Liberation Army Veterans. During this period, I observed many war victims with various symptoms of post traumatic stress disorder, in addition to their physical wounds.

It was then that I heard from members of our association about a programme—the Art of Living— being conducted in the rural areas of Kosovo that was significantly helping our members in their recovery. The men who had undergone the courses reported that they felt improved health, functioning, thinking and peacefulness. I contacted the local Art of Living personnel and arranged for them to conduct a course with a group of about forty severely disabled veterans.

I myself took part in the course and have experienced great relief from anger, irritability, sleep difficulties, flashbacks and depression since, and also witnessed more healing in many who have taken the course. I contacted the Mother Teresa Association and organized a multi-ethnic basic course for 105 residents of the Plemetina camp in Kosovo. The course participants were Albanians, Serbs and Romanians who were going through war trauma. They experienced peace and improved health during and after the workshop.

Born in a land whose heredity is full of trauma and war, I have continuously looked for a silent and peaceful corner to keep warm my soul and body. Guruji has shown me the way to that corner which was inside of me, and I have dedicated my life to help others find the same peaceful corner of love and joy that lies in each of us.

In 2003, I was told by doctors that I had lung cancer. I took the advanced course in summer. After many sessions of meditation and of being taken good care of by the Ayurvedic treatment staff in Bad Antogast, my health started improving day by day. Every day, Guruji would ask me how I felt. His love and care were the sweetest medicine. He told me not to worry, but to breathe, meditate and laugh. When I returned home, the doctors said, 'No cancer, just a few pieces of metal from grenades in your lungs!' and I said, 'No cigarettes for the rest of my life!' I easily quit smoking.

In the last few years, six attempts have been made on my life. Each time, I discovered the danger and nothing happened to me. I feel protected. However, Ananda, a wonderful teacher from Germany, full of love and care, made me write a letter to Guruji, describing all these events. Guruji replied to me: 'Be careful, but do not worry!' Since then, nothing bad has happened, and the threatening emails and phone calls have stopped.

Sri Sri's programmes helped trauma victims in Kosovo to live peacefully within a multi-ethnic society by providing them with tools to reawaken tolerance, reconciliation and acceptance. He also inspired dialogue between Albanians and Macedonians by widening the circle of belongingness from the narrow identities defined by ethnic and national boundaries.

The success of the Art of Living courses has also been due to the initiative shown by different government departments that have adopted this unique programme as a tool to heal their people.

Around 140 UN Police Peacekeepers have taken the Art of Living basic course in Kosovo. Commander of UNMIK Special Police Unit, Major S. K. Singh, said, 'We really felt the change within ourselves. The course gave us immense satisfaction and brought back happiness. During the course, our hearts and souls were at peace and we also felt the effects while discharging our official duties.'

Dr Ferid Agani, director of the Department of Strategic Planning and former focal point for mental health in the Ministry of Health has written a letter to Dr Hannu Vuori, principal international officer in the Ministry of Health saying, 'I was personally in a position to recognize the benefits accrued by my patients who underwent the treatment provided by the Art of Living therapists. I suggest that we begin with Art of Living involvement in programmes of community-based mental health centres, and later expand to public, government and UNMIK institutions.'

The Ministry of Health has joined hands with the Art of Living to conduct its programmes for its staff in all its mental health centres and hospitals. It also encourages the staff to get trained to become teachers of the BWS workshops. The ministry has found this to be a great programme, since it helps the participants to realize the peace within.

I was visiting the German ashram in Bad Antogast, a beautiful place nestled in the Black Forest. As I was walking, listening to the birds, their singing suddenly changed to the singing of what sounded to me like Sanskrit bhajans. The bus load of these people, I was sure, was headed for the ashram and I hurried to see who these happy people were. Getting out of the bus was my friend Sanja who had just arrived with the participants from Kosovo for the advanced course that was going to start the next day. I asked her whether it would be possible to speak to some of the people regarding their experiences if they were willing to share them. In response to my request, these wonderful people opened their hearts to me. This is what Nexhmedin shared with me:

> I am a twenty-six-year-old from Kosovo, married, with a son. During the beginning of the wars in the Balkans, I found myself in the Serbian army, fighting against the Croats. From that army, I ran away to Bosnia where I joined the Muslim army. There I went through the worst moments of my life, even lying in a mass grave among dead bodies. From that place, I ran away to Kosovo and joined the Kosovo army to fight against the Serbian army. When the war ended, I wandered through the mountains bordering Albania, completely lost and unable to return to my family and begin a normal life. I was wounded in the spine and was not able to walk without crutches. However, the most serious consequence I was suffering from was PTSD, manifested as epileptic attacks several times a day and long periods of amnesia and loss of consciousness. When I finally returned home, my family was desperate because of my condition and, when doctors were unable to help me, they persuaded me to attend the Art of Living course.
>
> During the course, I started feeling so much better that I travelled to another city with the teachers and went through the basic course once again. After the course, all the PTSD symptoms disappeared! There were no more epileptic attacks, amnesia, or loss of consciousness! All this within a span of two weeks only! After one month, I came to learn Sahaj Samadhi meditation without crutches! With a smile on my face, I told everyone that I had been practising regularly and did not need crutches any longer! Now I have a great desire to meet Guruji.

During the course of my conversations, I heard, over and over again, the same refrain of gratitude for the healing experienced by those suffering in body, mind and soul, thanks to the grace of one of the greatest masters of modern age, who has taken the ancient knowledge of India to the West as a tool of healing and as an instrument of peace. Here is what a few of the other participants had to say:

Zyrafete Hashani, psycho-social advisor, mental health centre in Ferizaj:

> At the beginning of the course, I experienced so much stress release that I did not feel comfortable. I was thinking of giving up the course. Now, I am happy that I stayed till the end of the course and gave myself the opportunity to enjoy the state of lightness and joy that followed after the process of purification. The Art of Living course is a wonderful knowledge and every individual should have it.

Flora Lleshi:

> I have been working as a nurse for seventeen years and I love my job. After the war, I suffered from depression caused by war and the loss of my child after birth. I used to worry a lot about the future of my daughters. The Art of Living has taught me to live in the present moment, and has lifted the big burden of worries that I lugged around.

Roza Sulaj:

> I have been working as a nurse for the last twenty-two years. In the beginning, I hesitated to come to this course but now I do not regret the decision. The Art of Living has relieved me from the painful memories of the death of my father and family members. I was traumatized when my father and two brothers were burnt and two relatives disappeared in the war. We still do not know where they are. Five years have passed since the tragedy

befell us, but only now have I learnt how to live life in
the present moment and be happy.

Naser Lumi, medical worker:

I am a massacre witness and former war prisoner. I was
beaten and tortured, and my legs and arms were broken
while I was in prison. On five occasions, I was even was
forced to play Russian roulette with colt pistol. The Art
of Living course has taught me how to live in the present
moment and forgive and move forward, carrying the
message of peace and love to the world.

Hanife Hoxha:

On 17 April 1999, I witnessed the massacre of 118
Albanians in Grashtica. We were forced to leave our
homes. We had no food. I saw paramilitary soldiers
taking out people from the line and killing them. When
I close my eyes, I still see a group of helpless young
people who were taken to a house to be massacred. The
Art of Living course has brought me great relief from
flashbacks. I fall asleep without a lot of effort, without
seeing scenes of massacre. The breathing exercises
have been very helpful in bringing my mind back to
the present.

Chechnya

As part of the Art of Living programme 'A Caucasus Free of
Stress', having received blessings from Sri Sri, a 'super' team of
Art of Living teachers—Alexei Morozov, Nina Nesterova, Alla
Shevchenko, Stas Gemes—and organizers—Anisa Akhmedova,
Katrin Hertog and Irina Mikhailovskaya—set off to conduct the
workshops in the extremely volatile area of Chechnya. They had
made connection ahead of time with the people in the region and,
being careful to be respectful of the local traditions in that area

of the Caucasus, prepared to take the healing methods to this part of the planet that had known a lot of strife and suffering due to war and conflict.

The following are Stas Geme's diary notes about his experiences with Chechens:

> When we arrived at the children's summer camp in the town of Nal'chike (in the Kabardino–Balkaria region of Chechnya) 600 Chechen children, and the parents and teachers accompanying them, stood before us. Their unusual world was full of adventure and the unexpected. Our own perception of reality changed over time as the Art of Living courses progressed.
>
> The children whom we taught, who became our friends during these five days, came from twelve different regions of Chechnya (including cities, villages, and mountainous regions). All of them had lived through war, forced migration and deprivation. Many don't understand the Russian language and, if at all, they rarely go to school.
>
> On the first day, we could sense their distrust for us and fear of Russian people in general. We also saw a total absence of discipline, as evidenced by the way they responded only when their teachers screamed and gave harsh commands.
>
> They also mistrusted each other. We felt a total inability among the children from different parts of Chechnya to communicate, as well as a lack of pride regarding their own nationality and culture. In the beginning, they were afraid to—simply unable to—close their eyes. It seemed as though by engaging in constant conversation with each other during the course meetings, they were trying to avoid the frightening and unfamiliar silence inside. The primary means of persuasion during arguments between the boys was the show of physical strength, whether fighting fairly or unfairly.
>
> The first 'strike' of love was experienced by Aleksei, Irina and Anisa, who had two groups of ninety children

each (180 Chechen children from 6–15 years of age, 150 of whom were boys). Simultaneously, Nina Nesterova began to lead the Art of Living course for the adults, in separate groups for men and women. Among the participants was a father–son pair of master karate sportsmen from the town of Shali, as well as a famous Chechen singer, composer and poetess. Within four days, the entire camp was singing 'Ganesha Sharanam', a famous song dedicated to Ganesha, the beloved Indian deity. Also, all the Chechen children were simply thrilled by the bhajan 'jaya guru, deva guru, om namo narayana'. They simply surrounded the singers on the stage and clapped as if, of all the songs they had ever heard, these were their very favourite. They also really liked the children's kriya. They saw it as a game of sounds and rhythms and practised the whole of it with great pleasure and with all their heart and soul. One couldn't help merging, as well, in the vibrant atmosphere of their melodious and rhythmic chorus.

And not one day passed without the Chechen 'Lezginki' (a national folk dance). When the first sounds of this graceful, happy, and noble dance were heard, whether during or after the course sessions, everyone simply leapt from their places and formed a circle ... and a new life began! The children forgot about everything; they loved this dance as if they had found the meaning of life in it. We couldn't resist joining in this beautiful and joyful excursion into another world and merged into the dancing circle. It seemed to us that even if the dance had lasted twenty-four hours, not one person would have left the circle to go anywhere.

All the children liked the course so much that when it ended, they came up to us and asked when the continuation would be. We learnt a lot from these beautiful children who were like our own. We felt Sri Sri's presence in every child who was testing our patience, sincerity, and faith in the power of love. The hearts of the young boys opened every time we went up to each one and, looking into their eyes, showing them due respect, extended our hand with the greeting 'Sallam Alleikum'. Then we would slap each other's palms and, with shining eyes, they would answer 'Valleikum Assallam' equally respectfully, yet with a tinge of a child's impulsiveness. Within only a few days, we felt as though all 600 children were members of our own family, our closest loved ones. And it seemed to us that we had become their most beloved and dependable fathers and mothers, brothers and sisters. They liked it when we held their shoulders and simply talked with them. Some of the children decided that they wanted to become Art of Living teachers and felt very proud to give an interview to our filmmaker and journalist friend, Arkadii.

With the beautiful melody of Sahils' bhajan from the album 'Narayana', the course ended with the children lifting their arms and swaying together in one unified line of singing and dancing. Seeing this beautiful dance and song, the words simply leapt out of my mouth: 'You are all one unified, happy Chechen family!' The eyes of the teachers from Chechnya shone with pleasure and contentment. This was the first time they had ever heard words of support and trust for the Chechen people, and for Chechen children, coming from the mouths of Russians who were singing the praises of their people's beauty and oneness.

At the end of the course, each child received a stuffed animal toy. They were so enraptured that it seemed this was the first toy they had received in many, many years. Then these children, who had become like our own, left to go to their twelve separate regions of Chechnya, carrying light, love and peace in their hearts.

After returning to Moscow, I telephoned one of my new Chechen friends, Emil, a boy of about fifteen years of age, and asked him how he was doing. He answered, 'Teacher! I have been practising for two days now and guess who is with me all the time? Sri Sri Ravi Shankar!'

Combating Violence Using Non-violent Ways in Africa

'A wave of peace and non-violence needs to be created in the entire African continent, which, I feel, would start from South Africa,' Sri Sri said once. 'Every individual needs to take responsibility for his or her life and to do that, one needs enormous strength that can only come from spirituality. Today we need a spirituality which unites people from all religious backgrounds.'

The rural community of the Eastern Cape answered this call through the signing of a partnership between the House of Traditional Leaders and the Art of Living Foundation. The partnership will implement Africa's first Programme for Rural Development (PRD), a revolutionary programme designed in India which has touched over 25,000 villages in that country.

The PRD was inaugurated at Mngqesha Great place by King Sandile of the Rharhabe Kingdom, the Eastern Cape premier, Mrs Balindlela, and Sri Sri on his official visit to South Africa at the invitation of the government in December 2006 to be an honoured guest at the culmination of the year-long 'Satyagraha 100' celebrations. The celebrations commemorated the centenary of the launch of Mahatma Gandhi's *satyagraha* campaign.

Nationally, a hundred youngsters were selected for a Youth Leadership Training programme (YLTP) conducted by the Art of Living. The aim of the programme was to train unemployed youth to become catalysts of change within their communities. These youth enrolled for the ten-day residential training programme, where the values of self-motivation, self-discipline, service to the community, community empowerment and related issues are inculcated. They were trained in leadership and communication skills, and social mobilization techniques. The other aims of the programme were building their confidence, strengthening their personal and emotional development, and making music and celebration a part of daily living. The enthusiasm and confidence that the programme developed was the key to transformation.

A major component of the course included teaching students how to build a community from within. The youngsters were monitored for a period of eight weeks. Field training took place, where they utilized the skills learnt in the first phase.

Phase II of the training was again a ten-day residential programme where problem-solving skills, interpersonal skills and various other management techniques were taught. This time, the emphasis was on the development of human resources as well as sustainable social and economic development. This phase also covered vocational training, ranging from project management, recycling, AIDS awareness and organic gardens to operating systems such as Ubuntu and principles of citizenship. Once the training was completed, forty youth graduated as youth leaders, and many of the ongoing projects have emerged after the training, through them.

It was not easy for the Art of Living to get as well-established as it is today in Africa. I was talking with Rakhee Vithal, a young mother, who for some time has been working with the community on a variety of projects. She is a dedicated disciple and seva warrior of Sri Sri Ravi Shankar. Rakhee's involvement with Sri Sri's initiatives started a few years ago when she started wondering: 'What can I do to make life more meaningful in our society?'

The answer came in an unusual way.

A graduate in international relations and politics, she had been working for some years when stress started to affect her health. Worn out and tired, she knew she had to do something. Then she heard of a foundation called the Art of Living.

'I thought I'd go and try the classes and see what happened,' she says. 'We were shown some special breathing techniques, which I quickly mastered. Amazingly, the effects were immediate. I instantly felt better.'

Impressed, she decided to investigate. Who was the person behind the Art of Living, and how did he come to devise such a simple yet successful programme?

Her journey of discovery took her to India, where she met Sri Sri Ravi Shankar and realized that there was much more to this remarkable man than breathing techniques. The young South African was immediately drawn to Shankar's teachings. In the years that followed, Rakhee was to return to India ten times to learn more.

'The first time I was in the presence of the master, I couldn't speak,' she recalls. 'No words would come and I just cried and cried. I kept going back to learn more. Through the years, he guided me to the point where I knew what I had to do. I had to return to South Africa and take the knowledge I had gathered to others.'

That journey was not to be an easy one.

According to the World Health Organization, poor communities are extremely vulnerable to stress, which manifests itself as depression, with related physical symptoms. Vithal felt drawn to help the poor in her own community, and that meant going to the townships where the need was greatest.

'Studies show that the costs of mental and physical health actually worsen the economic condition of a country, setting up a vicious cycle of poverty and mental stress,' Rakhee says. But where could she, a lone woman without connections in the townships, start?

'I went to Soweto and started talking to the people on the streets,' she says.

She made progress when she started working with youth organizations. At first just a few joined her groups but slowly the word spread. The young people were filled with energy and obviously enjoyed the workshops. And youth like Bongani Mashnini, 26, from Vosloorus, came forward to organize further courses. Bongani works for the South African Youth Council, doing peer education in colleges in the townships. He organizes workshops and events to talk about sex education, AIDS, cancer, etc. He is also an executive in a youth organization called New Age Environment and Recreation South Africa, which organizes workshops on leadership training and conflict management. He says:

> Art of Living has done a lot for me. I did not have focus, and didn't know where I was going. I used to drink and smoke a lot too. Now I am very focussed. I used to be quite unstable and had many girlfriends, but my mind is calm now and I have just one girlfriend. I've seen a lot of changes in myself. I lost my sister and my mother, but I don't feel that I'm alone any more, I feel like I'm part of a huge family. The YLTP is what changed my life. When we came back, I noticed how people just greet me on the streets. They can see that life in you, that light in you.

Rakhee describes Breath-Water-Sound as a simple yet dynamic programme. It teaches participants to manage their emotions and stress. The BWS courses have been taught in the disadvantaged communities from 2000 onwards. The course is taught by Art of Living teachers and volunteers, and more recently by the YLTP youth leaders. But, says Rakhee, the major component of the course is community development and empowerment. The emphasis is on health and nutrition. The BWS often initiates community projects for the betterment of the community and to help uplift the needy in the area. She says:

> Some wonderful projects are underway. The need for computer centres was one we identified and we approached a few corporates to sponsor computers. We have run empowerment courses for our youth leaders and taught local women such basic skills as pickle-making, a useful way of generating income. We even managed to get mangoes, spices and oil sponsored. We have started organic farming initiatives too. Food has an enormous impact on the mind, so we approached the local authority for land that the residents could use for growing vegetables. We'd like to see a garden in every home.

Art of Living and the Gauteng Department of Food Security developed a partnership. Training was conducted in Dobsonville, Soweto, for a hundred BWS participants in organic food gardens. The only criterion for getting training was that the participants must have undergone the BWS programme. The department provided the training, equipment, seedlings and a six-month follow-up training programme.

Motherhood did not hinder Vithal's work. After her baby was born, she continued working on all sorts of projects. 'It's amazing how eager people are to come and do something for their community,' she says. Art of Living volunteers started teaching BWS in Chatsworth at the Nelson Mandela Youth Centres over a year ago. It was targeted at school going children as well as youth. The centre runs an anti-drug forum. BWS, along with Sri Sri Yoga, has subsequently become a component of this forum. Drug users as well as peddlers undergo the BWS, and it has been a success story. One of the participants shared that the Art of Living course has taught them how to say 'no' to drugs.

Tulisile Mcanyana, 23, from Verilam, works in a shop as a saleswoman. She teaches BWS to elderly women and at high schools. She says:

> We've had good feedback, especially from the school kids who say they are more focussed in their studies, more respectful and not as reckless as before. They are settling down and are more responsible with their school work.
>
> The first time I was introduced to Art of Living, I was very stressed because of my life experiences. I've become a new person after doing the course. In short, I was born again. I am now a person that can be with anybody, anywhere. I am at peace, my mind is always calm and I can handle difficult people much more easily. I am also able to cope with my workload much more easily, and don't become as stressed. The course has worked magic!
>
> If this knowledge can go around the world, it will be a better place to live … an amazing place, rather.

Everyone will be at peace, talking to each other. There will be no violence, no killing.

My dream for my community is to take all the kids off the streets. I'd like to show them that life is not what they think it is. I'd like them to go back to school, be nice to their parents, and grow to be people we can rely on. I want them to know that they are flesh and blood too, that they can still change. I'd like to help them change.

One Sunday morning, people started gathering at a camp in Dobsonville. It was a bright sunny day—perfect picnic weather—but the arrivals were not in holiday mood.

The word had spread in the area that a medical camp was being held. So the sick came, hoping that one of the experts will diagnose their ailment or, at least, counsel and advise them. They found a place and sat down to wait for their turn.

The medical camp in Dobsonville was set up when local youth informed us about the need for some form of medical consultation. Rakhee approached an array of professionals, requesting them to volunteer their services for just a day, thereby providing the sick with guidance and diagnosis. The camp was set up.

'It was an unbelievable experience,' Vithal said later. 'With the help of Dr Anita Khoosal and other medical experts, we were able to counsel 207 patients that day.'

'We realized, however, that we had touched just the tip of the iceberg. There are many problems related to eating habits, breathing and sleeping patterns, etc. HIV/AIDS counselling is also needed quite urgently; which is why we are arranging another camp soon, where a prominent virologist has agreed to come and help.'

Farida Ismail, a sixty-year-old who works for the Department of Health as a coordinator of homecare for tuberculosis and HIV patients, says:

I've been all over in search of the truth and I've read many books. It was after my return from a trip to

Malaysia, Bangkok and Singapore, and after having visited all the temples there that I walked back to my office and found a pamphlet on Sri Sri Ravi Shankar. The picture caught my eye because it so reminded me of pictures of Jesus Christ.

After doing the programme, I found that a great weight had been lifted off my shoulders. I felt alive again. I got rid of the arthritis that was creeping in and stopped taking my asthma pump and pills. I started to enjoy the things that gave me pleasure before arthritis had crept in. My zest for living came alive.

Being a Muslim, I have found that my daily prayers have become much more meaningful after doing the Art of Living course. I do the breathing exercises and chanting using Arabic words. The breath control has been in harmony with my heart beat and has made my prayers a lot more powerful and deep, and therefore more beneficial.

On the other hand, in Johannesburg, Chandranan 'Chintz' Bahna is tackling an even more difficult project: helping prisoners. He goes regularly to Leeuwkop prison to teach stress management to inmates and individuals on parole. He is part of a programme called 'Prison SMART (Stress Management and Rehabilitative Training)', details of which I will go into later. He is so committed to self-development and rehabilitative training in prisons that he sacrificed his full-time job to work on the project. He asked the company he worked for, SA Breweries, if he could work part-time so that he could concentrate on the Prison SMART programme.

Chintz, who became a teacher at the same time as Namrita and me, and who we remember to have been a happy and cheerful person even then, refuses to accept that working with prisoners is a stressful job. 'I have had the most amazing experiences with them and love every moment I spend with them. The programme exists to help prisoners in their personal rehabilitation,' he says. 'It is there to reduce violence and drug dependence in prisons and in society. We do this by teaching essential life skills that help individuals to accept responsibility for their past actions and to handle future conflict situations successfully.'

How does he feel working with tough criminals?

'I feel protected, rather than threatened by them,' he says. 'There are some beautiful people trying to escape the aggression that has become an intrinsic feature of their lives.' And he is there as an instrument of Sri Sri to offer them the solace they seek.

Apart from them, Art of Living has other young and dedicated volunteers working as hard and selflessly as Rakhee and Chintz to bring healing, love and a sense of belonging into others' lives. Deepali, a beautiful young girl, is one such volunteer who, inspired by her guru, Sri Sri Ravi Shankar, gave up her comfortable life in Mumbai to travel to war and terror infested areas. She did wonderful work in the north-eastern states of India and is now in Africa, in the Ivory Coast, taking the message of love and peace to those in need.

Côte d'Ivoire or Ivory Coast, as it is commonly referred to, is a beautiful country in West Africa. Unfortunately, this region and Cameroon, also on the western coast of Africa, has been witnessing conflict for many years. In Côte d'Ivoire, discrimination and economic deprivation are two of the several issues which have given birth to other problems. A two-year civil war, which began in 2002, saw the division of the country into a rebel-led north and government-led south. There has been a complete breakdown of economy and infrastructure and has led to the spread of disease and poor health. The country had been witnessing turmoil even prior to the civil war. At present, it is still grappling with the eddies of its troubled past.

The Art of Living Foundation's work in Ivory Coast began way back in 1999 under the guidance of Sir Sri. These efforts were however halted temporarily owing to the widespread tension in the region, only to begin with renewed vigour in 2002 and continues till today. A team of teachers, locals as well as from India and France, began conducting stress-elimination breath workshops and moved from village to village, counselling the traumatized. While imparting knowledge on coping with stress, the team educated the locals on hygiene and health, gave medicines to the underprivileged and motivated them to work for social harmony and upliftment. The Art of Living volunteers didn't limit their focus to just the victims of ethnic strife and attempted to treat the root cause. The people were moved. 'How can someone sitting far away in India care so much for us and send somebody to help us?' said Jean Claude, a local (referring to Sri Sri Ravi Shankar).

The Dioula and Guéré are two warring tribes in Deukoué. Differences over land and economic issues have caused such disharmony that one cannot walk in the village of the other without being attacked. The Art of Living team brought together fifteen youth from each warring faction for a YLTP. The eight days spent in the course transformed their outlook irreversibly. It helped build a sense of trust; and so, a step was taken towards eliminating their conflicts. 'We lived together and discovered that our ways were very similar. There is no fear. We're brothers,' said Adama, a member of the Dioula tribe after doing the course. As a peace initiative, the members of one tribe are handing over a village which they had forcibly taken over. What's even more heartening is that they are rebuilding all the homes and readying the area before inviting the others in. Besides inter-community harmony, the youth started implementing the Art of Living's 5H programme which focusses on health, homes, hygiene, human values and harmony in diversity. They have been inspired to take responsibility for their villages and are engaged in cleanliness campaigns and repairing roads.

Through stress-elimination and a new vision for the community, the locals have been infused with a new spirit of life. Community initiatives have given the people a better quality of life. Locals who reported suffering from bouts of malaria several times every few months, became malaria-free. Young boys and girls who required alcohol to shut out the horrific memories of the civil war were able to sleep peacefully without the aid of external supports.

In November 2007, another YLTP was conducted for forty Ivorians in Man, a region bordering Liberia and a gateway of violence between Liberia and Ivory Coast. In a picturesque locale, set between mountains and forests, the participants were taught yoga, stress-elimination breath techniques and meditation. After these intensive programmes and counselling, the participants brainstormed on ways in which they could contribute to community development.

Through the experiences shared by the participants, it was clear that they had a new direction in life. A lady who had lost all desire to live after her husband's murder confessed that she was on the brink of suicide before coming to the course and that she got a fresh perspective to life after the course.

Another man said that he had become a racist after the war and would not open his door to anyone who was not from his tribe. Yet, after spending eight days with people from many different tribes, he realized that all are one. His door has never remained shut since.

These experiences reflect the phenomenal transformation that occurs when the individual is free from trauma and inhibitions. When individuals feel responsible as agents of change and join hands to bring in the change, the community progresses and so does the society.

Recognizing the effectiveness of the Art of Living projects, the minister of reconciliation in Ivory Coast personally lends support to the work initiated by Sri Sri. At a meeting between the administration and sixty non-governmental organizations, everyone wanted to forge an association with the foundation.

On 1 December 2007, a peace conference was held in Duékoué. In attendance were Djedje Dano Sebastien, minister of national reconciliation and his wife Patricia Dano Sebastien, Mr Tihi Kpao Victor, mayor of Duékoué, the police commissioner of Duékoué, the iman of Duékoué, youth leaders and village heads.

The minister shared how most NGOs came to see him with very impressive projects and big budgets. However, almost all these projects landed up in a drawer and never saw the light of day. Art of Living was one of the very few NGOs that went ahead and took the initiative to reach out to the most troubled areas of Ivory Coast without waiting for anyone. He said, 'Sri Sri's initiatives consider human beings in their entirety, and heal the body, mind and spirit. The Art of Living is one of the rare NGOs which works at the grass-root level, close to the population and goes to the core of the problem.'

The mayor of Duékoué, was so impressed with the work done by the local youth leaders trained by the foundation that he pledged support for all their future projects. Most significantly, every individual believed that what they had once dreamt of—peace and progress—were achievable.

The local youth leaders shared how misunderstandings between the different tribes had caused the war to reach this point. They pointed out that it was the initiatives taken by the Art of Living youth that had helped cool the situation. Many youth came and shared how, before the YLTP, their minds were closed to people from other tribes, especially after the war. However after undergoing the programme they saw how pointlessly they had spent their time, energy and resources in fighting with each other when ultimately it boiled down to the fact that they were all part of the same family. Some shared how the Art of Living programme had brought peace to their minds and lives and how all the trauma and hatred caused by the war had been erased. They felt so much at peace that many of them had even become intermediaries to solve the problems between different tribes in the villages and were now called the 'wise' of the villages.

 *Chapter Six*

Healing the Victims of Terrorism

Sri Sri often says, 'Inside every culprit is a victim crying for help. If you heal the victim, you will eliminate crime from the planet.' Most people baulk at words like compassion, love and understanding when used for terrorists because they feel strongly that terrorists need to be taught the lesson they deserve in order to keep society safe.

An act which is only destructive and inflicts suffering, both on oneself and others, is terrorism. In such acts, human values are lost in the process of trying to achieve goals. Terrorists are motivated people, ready to put their lives at risk and fight for a cause. They are not in it for the money but to get their voices heard. They feel that their only option is to take to the gun, to bomb and to resort to suicide attacks. However the experience of those who have done the Art of Living workshop with even the most hardened terrorists has been that reaching out to them with compassion and offering effective solutions helped them to break out of the vicious cycle of crime and violence.

This is what Mohammed Afroze, a Kashmiri militant against whom POTA charges were withdrawn recently, told the gathering at barrack number six on the first floor of Byculla prison, Mumbai. 'The course has brought me immense peace. I no longer get angry, nor do I have anything against anyone. When I'm out of prison, I would like to teach this course to my family and community members.' This was towards the end of the Art of Living workshop and he was sharing his experiences with the rest of the participants as is normally done on the last day of the course. In fact, the course was the reason cited by Afroze for refusing bail. The authorities are so impressed with the change that has come over these prisoners that they hope that the prisoners will keep this discipline when they leave prison since they feel it will help them lead normal lives and stay on the path of peace.

This is what Sri Sri had to say to my questions on fanaticism and terrorism:

> Terrorism is the ignorance in us that makes us petty-minded. Fanaticism and rigidity take you far away from divinity. Those who profess fanaticism do not need condemnation, but compassion. Terrorism induces fear and increases poverty, suffering and loss of life, with no apparent gain to anyone. Instead of offering or seeking solutions, terrorism looks to destruction as an answer. In acts of terrorism, human values are lost.

When asked why people turn to terrorism, Sri Sri had this to say:

> The first factor is frustration and desperation to achieve a goal. When people are desperate to achieve some goal and are unable to do it, the desperation brings up the violence in them. The second factor is belief in a non-verifiable concept of merit and heaven. 'If I die fighting for god, then I will go to heaven, because god wants this act to happen.' Who knows? No one can verify these statements. The third is a staunch belief that 'my way is the only way'. The fourth is choosing to ignore human values in order to achieve a goal and the fifth is the lack of respect or honour for life itself.
>
> Terrorism is based on a concept of god as favouring some and being angry with others. This notion undermines the omnipresence and omnipotence of god. How can an omnipresent god exclude some people? How can an omnipotent god be angry? Anger and frustration arise when someone is unable to do something or control

something. With this limited idea of god, you become the saviour of god rather than the servant of god. God is a poor fellow sitting somewhere, getting angry, and you are trying to help him. Terrorism fails to recognize that god loves variety and diversity; that many different schools of thought exist in this world. Terrorism does not respect or honour life. Terrorism arises when someone identifies himself first and foremost as a member of a particular religion or community and then feels ready to give up his life for that limited identity. What we need is to identify ourselves as part of the Divine first and, after that, as part of humanity.

In India

SIMI

One wonders what the psyche of a fundamentalist is. What is it that spurs him on his mission of hatred? How should one deal with such a person? We were lucky to witness an interaction between a handful of SIMI activists and Sri Sri a couple of years ago. We felt that the same would be of relevance and could serve as an eye-opener in the current scenario. The backdrop for this occasion was one of Sri Sri's tours of Kerala. A series of *Anandotsavams* had been planned in various cities of Kerala to coincide with Sri Sri's visit to those cities. Sri Sri's visit was expected to attract huge crowds running into several hundred thousands. A week before the tour commenced, towards the end of November, there was a surprise in store. The newspapers announced that SIMI (Students Islamic Movement of India) had called for a general strike all over Kerala on December 6, the day being an anniversary of the Babri Masjid demolition. Coincidentally, an Anandotsavam had been planned on December 6 in Thrissur, the cultural capital of Kerala. The police also warned that they had received bomb threats. However, when contacted, Sri Sri assured Xavier, the president of the organizing committee that the satsang will be held. On December 6, though the newspapers had announced that the function was cancelled and the police had withdrawn their permission due to the bomb scare, a crowd numbering more than a lakh attended the satsang.

The following day, Sri Sri gave an audience to a few SIMI leaders. Four leaders came to meet Sri Sri at the residence of one of the organizers. They (the SIMI leaders) were dashing youths in their mid-twenties. One of them was carrying the holy Koran. They were a little stern and stiff. Their eyes were fixed and seemed to reflect an inner fire. They looked prepared to repulse anything that Sri Sri would tell them. Sri Sri was his usual smiling self.

The stage was set. It had all the signs of a classic confrontation. On one side were the brash youth—intemperate, impatient, driven by ideology and out to prove their superiority; on the other was a youthful, learned sage, unperturbed, offering sane explanations that echoed an uncommon depth and breadth of understanding. All of us in the room were eager to see how Sri Sri would deal with these firebrands. Sri Sri embraced them and offered them chairs to sit. There was not an iota of change in his attitude. A casual onlooker could be forgiven for thinking that Sri Sri considered these gentlemen to be amongst his most ardent devotees. For us, it was yet another opportunity to witness the unconditional love that Sri Sri exemplifies.

The leader of the group spoke first.

SIMI: You had wanted to meet us.

Sri Sri: Yes. I wanted to understand why your organization was opposed to the Anandotsavam.

SIMI: We thought that holding an Anandotsavam on December 6 was a deliberate move to insult our religious sentiments. Do you know about our religion? Do you believe in the Koran at all?

Sri Sri: Yes, of course.

SIMI (not expecting this answer, pointing to the Koran, they shot the next question): We believe that the Koran is the only source of knowledge. What about you?

Sri Sri: The Koran is one among the various kinds of knowledge revealed to man from time to time.

SIMI: But god has said this is the only knowledge. The way of the Koran is the only way. There is no other way.

Sri Sri: This message can be found in the scriptures of all religions. The Vedas say, *'naanyah panthaah ayanaaya vidyate'* which means that there is no other way but the way of Truth! The same is said in the Bible; Jesus says, 'To go to my father, you have to go through me. I am the only way.'

SIMI: But our scripture says worshipping any form or idol is evil, it is blasphemy.

Sri Sri: What is Good and Evil after all? It is relative. Relative existence is not the complete picture. For example, milk is good, but too much milk can kill you. Poison is harmful, but a drop of poison can save your life. Most life-saving medicines have poison written on them! These are neither absolutely good nor bad; they are just there. Truth transcends duality, and god is the absolute and only Truth. So, where is the place for evil?

SIMI: Yet you Hindus worship many gods, whereas our view is that there is only one god and his message is what is required to go to heaven.

Sri Sri: There is only one god in many forms.

SIMI (restless and unwilling to listen to any explanation, they interrupted Sri Sri): But the Koran says you should only worship Allah, who is formless, whereas the Hindus worship idols which are only stones.

Sri Sri: Do you honour the Koran?

SIMI (a little taken aback at this question from Sri Sri and with a righteous air): Yes, it is god's word!

Sri Sri: Do you honour the Mecca?

SIMI: Yes, of course! That is our sacred place.

Sri Sri: So also, Hindus honour god's creation as god. Just like sound (Koran), the crescent moon, the Kaaba and the month of Ramadan are sacred for you, Hindus consider the Ganga, the

Himalayas and their saints as sacred. See, a picture of your daughter is *not* your daughter, but you still adore the daughter's picture. When you see the picture, aren't you reminded of your daughter?

The SIMI leaders nodded in agreement.

Sri Sri: So also, a symbol is not god but is honoured as god. This sense of honouring the sacredness of the symbol makes you awake and alive. That is why the ancient *rishis* advised everyone to see all of god's creation and your whole life as sacred. They considered god as omnipresent and his creation as inseparable from him; like the dance and the dancer.

The spirit loves diversity. Is there only one type of vegetable or fruit? God created many varieties of fruit and vegetables. There is not just one type of tree, not just one type of snakes, clouds, mosquitoes ... even *you* change your attire for different occasions. So how could this consciousness, that manifested this whole creation, be monotonous? There is only one God in many forms. Only one God is advocated. When you accept the variety in divinity, you cease to be a fanatic and fundamentalist.

A pregnant silence filled the room as the SIMI leaders looked at each other expecting the other to speak. Then as a face-saving measure, the SIMI leader replied, 'I will need to go and consult other scholars.' With a compassionate expression on his face, Sri Sri said with a wave of his hand: 'Never mind, forget about religion. We are all human beings. Let us have a peaceful society. Let us focus on development.'

SIMI: No, no! What are you saying? You are talking about *this* world. What we do here is immaterial. The Koran tells us that what matters is what you get in eternal life and that we need not worry about material life. By doing service to the society, you will simply remain here. You have to obey Allah. Allah is the only god and Mohammed is the last prophet.

Sri Sri: Do you think the Sikh gurus are not prophets? Isn't Mirabai a prophet? What about Chaitanya Mahaprabhu?

Once again, there was silence. Their expressions had changed. The rigidity had weakened and in its place was some uncertainty.

Sri Sri seemed totally at ease, unmindful of the challenges posed to him.

SIMI: No! You can go to heaven only if you believe in Allah and the Koran.

Sri Sri: No my dear, there was Buddha, Mahavira, Nanak, Jesus, Shankara ... do you think they are not in heaven? If not, then I would rather be with them!

SIMI: You are such a nice person, but we pity you because you cannot get the truth. You can't go to Allah. You won't be rewarded by Allah. God will never show mercy on you.

Sri Sri: Never mind (with a mischievous smile), I will be with these people (Shankara, Jesus, etc.).

Even as we were admiring Sri Sri's patience and objectivity, we were concerned at the wrong indoctrination that these youths had been subjected to. We also observed that a few others in the room were getting restive too, possibly wondering why Sri Sri was spending so much time with these people who were obviously not receptive to his ideas, and all this when hundreds were waiting outside just for a glimpse of him.

SIMI: Do you know that over 1400 years ago, in the middle of the desert, god revealed the secrets of creation. Even when there was no science, god said that the atom is the smallest particle!

Sri Sri (smiling): Yes, the same is there in the *shastras* too, which are known to have been written more than 10,000 years ago. In the shastras it is said that the earth is over nineteen billion years old! Truth is beyond time and space. It is not confined to one time or one place. One needs to have a scientific spirituality.

As if to conclude the conversation, Sri Sri gave them *ladoos* (Indian sweet) as *prasad* (offering). By now, there were traces of a smile on their faces. When they were about to leave, he gave them a hug. They definitely seemed to be less stern than earlier. Could their attitude have changed? We wondered whether this changed attitude, if we read it right, would persist or whether they would go back to their old fanatical ways. But one thing was for sure ... Sri Sri had made an impression that they would not forget!

The Art of Living courses have touched the lives of hundreds of terrorists, transforming their lives through practical, friendly and simple yet powerful techniques. It has helped them regain their self-esteem, break away from their victim mentality and to reintegrate with society. Says a Kashmiri terrorist, as reported by CNN-IBN in May 2006, 'When I came to the course, they asked me what I wanted and I had said that I wanted an AK-47. After doing this course, I only want to give love.'

Gujarat Riots

Riots have become a way of life in India. They pop up anywhere, any time, and people have to live with the morbid reality of the violence that riots bring with them. Sometimes nothing happens; sometimes, like it did in Gujarat in 2002, it causes mayhem and communities from both sides suffer intensely. As usual, Guruji's simple words soothe and enlighten us at the same time. The cause of the riots was the ongoing conflict between the Hindus and Muslims over the birthplace of Lord Rama. Sri Sri, who is involved as a mediator between the two communities, feels that the solution for the Ram Janmabhoomi–Babri Masjid issue should be sought outside the ambit of the Supreme Court to ensure communal harmony in the long run. Being in a civilized world, we cannot allow this 400-year-old problem to continue unsolved. Sri Sri, who visited the riot-torn state soon after the riots, identified the Ram temple issue as the root cause of Gujarat's violence. His mission was to find ways to restore the faith that both the communities had lost in each other. He said, 'The court verdict may decide the matter but the feeling of anger and hatred between the two communities could be detrimental to national interest. The issue could be sorted out through a dialogue between various religious heads and by keeping politicians out of the matter.' Talking about the current scenario in Gujarat, he said, 'Rather than blaming the culprits and levelling allegations against each other, it is necessary to address the needs and requirements of the victims, find the best possible way to rehabilitate them and to restore their confidence.'

During his visit, Sri Sri Ravi Shankar visited some of the refugee camps and spoke to the victims. He also met religious heads of the Muslim community in Ahmedabad. 'Time is short and we should not waste it in blaming each other,' he told them. He sought views on what should be done to bridge the gap between the two communities. He also met representatives of the Hindu community and conveyed the expectations of the other community.

According to Sri Sri, 'Mistakes have happened in the past. It is only wise to forgive and forget them. As a civilized society, we cannot afford not to practise forgiveness and start building trust for the betterment of the society and of the individual.' He appealed to people to restore the sense of social security and confidence among all religions. 'We have stayed and we have to stay together. Living separately is not possible,' he said, adding, 'The sooner we achieve it again, the better.'

His visit acted like balm on the wounds of those who suffered on both sides of the conflict. Many camps were held for the victims and aggressors on either side to bring peace back into their hearts and, in turn, to the state.

Mumbai Riots

Another city that, over the years, has seen many riots and has been engulfed in violence, the latest one just a few months ago, is Mumbai. Rajshree Patel, our dear friend with whom we did our first advance course in 1994 has this beautiful story to recount, of her experience of being caught in the midst of a riot and the faith that carried her through:

> The year was 1992. I had just finished a three-month stint of teaching in Gujarat. As soon as I returned, Sri

Sri asked me to go to Mumbai. 'You will have a blast,' he assured me. Thereafter he proceeded on his tour of Europe.

My first course was to take place in Chembur R.C.F. Colony, an area located right on the other side of town. On the second day of the course, I arrived home to be greeted with the news of a bomb blast in the Bombay Stock Exchange. By next morning, riots had broken out in the city. A limited curfew was brought into effect.

The family with whom I was staying tried to dissuade me from going to the course. I could see that they were concerned about my safety. Going there involved passing through a particularly vulnerable area where the riots were raging at their worst. But I was determined to go. It was my responsibility to be there even for the few participants who might turn up.

Since the family could not risk driving me to the venue, I went out looking for a cab. I found a lone one at the stand and asked the driver if he could take me to Chembur. He looked at me incredulously, not sure if he had heard right. I again asked if he would drive me there. He shook his head and said that it was impossible to go there. I kept cajoling him. He said that it would not be safe for me to go there alone. 'I am not alone,' I told him. He realized how earnest I was. 'Do you know what will happen to my vehicle and to me?' he asked me. 'Don't worry,' I told him. 'You will be safe, and so will your vehicle. Let's go now.' He looked directly into my eyes and something made him believe me.

As we drove on, the blazing signs of the riots were all over the streets. Buses and cars on fire, windows smashed to bits, people looting, police and military personnel everywhere. It was like a war zone. But a strange sense of calm kept me going till, finally, we were made to halt at a point. No cars were allowed to pass through that point. The cab driver told me that we would now have to turn back. 'In that case, drop me here,' I said. He refused to do that. Reluctantly, he drove up to the police officer on duty and told him that I wanted to drive to Chembur. 'What!' exclaimed the officer. Bending down to see who this 'senile' lady was, he looked at me intently. Once again, someone spoke to him through me and he rose up, saying, 'Okay, go, but hurry.'

Once we reached Chembur, I reassured the driver that nothing would happen to him on his way back. As I entered the house of one of my students, the phone rang. It was Sri Sri. 'Didn't I tell you that you would have a blast?' he remarked wryly. He was to return from Germany the next day and his ticket was via Mumbai. I urged him to get it altered as Mumbai was not safe. But he was completely unperturbed. 'I am sure you will find a way to take care,' he said, to which I replied, 'Will *I* or will *you?*'

He gave me his flight details and hung up the phone. I went to my course, and found that all sixty participants were waiting for me. The colony was a safe zone with secure boundary walls. A participant asked me if he could leave early. I said 'no'. At the end of the session, a woman invited me for tea at her place. As we walked towards her house, I noticed the same gentleman who had wanted to leave early a few feet ahead of me. He also turned towards the same house, which bore the sign: Commandant of Police. The woman with me explained that the man was her husband and that he had wanted to leave early because of the curfew. I asked the man if I could get any transport to go to the airport. He said that it would be impossible, since there were shoot at sight orders in the area. I explained why I needed to go there. He offered to arrange a police car for me.

His second-in-command accompanied me there. There was a security officer with us too. As we passed through one of the badly hit areas, I could smell the stench of burning flesh in the air, and sense people hiding behind burnt cars and in alleys, carrying sickles, sticks and other weapons. I noticed that a jeep was tailing us. There were more security officials there.

We arrived at the airport and I immediately spotted Sri Sri pushing his trolley out. I quickly got out of the car and moved towards him. As I greeted him, I heard the sound of a gun handle being pulled. Almost at once, there were three officers around me. 'See, you found a way,' said Sri Sri. We laughed and proceeded towards home.

Mumbai Train Blasts

Mumbai, the city that is constantly tested, was once again thrown into turmoil on 11 July 2006 when a series of seven bomb blasts took place over a period of eleven minutes on the suburban railway, the main form of transport for thousands of Mumbaikars. 209 people lost their lives and over 700 were injured in the attacks.

As usual, the Art of Living volunteers came forward to help the city get back on its feet with courage and dignity. Trauma relief programmes, including meditation sessions for victims and witnesses, are still being conducted by the Art of Living Foundation.

For many who had been on these trains and were witness to the chaos and suffering that followed the blasts, these workshops brought relief and healing. Some of these testimonies bear witness to the fact. 'Memories of the blast, the bleeding bodies and the screams haunted me for nights until my wife, Pushpa, finally forced me into attending this course that has rejuvenated my entire being,' said Dinesh Tirodkar. 'It was only after the meditation that Dinesh slept soundly an entire night,' Pushpa confirmed with a smile. 'After attending just a few sessions of the course, I am now geared to deal with any disaster with a smile. In fact, I boarded a local train from Goregaon to Malad to attend today's session,' said a beaming Vishwas Rao.

26/11

In the torturous sixty hours that left Mumbai burning and bleeding due to the 26/11 terror attacks, the worst affected were the staff of the three landmark hotels of the city, the Taj Mahal, the Trident and the Oberoi, who remained undaunted by the attacks, only to make their guests comfortable. Though the staff handled the situation with great efficiency and bravery, the trauma they experienced has left an indelible scar on their psyche.

In order to help them overcome the trauma of the ordeal, over a hundred hotel employees of the Oberoi and Trident hotels were put through an Art of Living course conducted by Sri Sri's Mumbai Art of Living teachers.

Says Ramesh Raman who coordinated the whole effort:

> We conducted an Art of Living course for the employees to help them get over the trauma of the attacks. The course stretched for over a period of three-and-a-half days, and dealt with teaching the participants to deal with a variety of emotions. The results were astounding and the directors of both the hotels wrote us letters of thanks and stressed how much it had helped relieve their employees of the terror and stress induced by the attacks.

Later, Sri Sri himself came to Mumbai and this is what he said:

> It is obvious that when the society is attacked and we lose our near and dear ones, it causes a lot of sorrow. It also causes fear. But if we keep wallowing in this sorrow and fear and the anger that comes along with it, then life moves towards the path to perdition. But if we want to channelize this energy and prepare to face this war bravely, we need to first calm the mind and come to a state of equanimity. We need to become samdarshi (one whose view is balanced and unbiased). Here, in Priyadarshini park [the venue], let's all pray

for those who have departed, and take a pledge to be samdarshi.

But we also need to come together and pledge that we shall work towards protecting our country. Let's also resolve to first examine the qualifications of those who we elect. We need social leaders who are *satyadarshi* (truthful), samdarshi (calm and unbiased), and *doordarshi* (farsighted). We need to protect our country from those who manipulate issues for their personal gains and lead by playing votebank politics.

Secondly, we need to resolve to not act out of anger, but instead channelize our dynamic energy for the betterment of the society. We also need to expose all those who support violence, no matter what religion they belong to. Sometimes, we protect those who are at fault. We must get rid of the mentality which asks us to protect people of our own religion or community even if they are doing wrong. This is very important. I would like to say to all the families who have lost their dear ones that the soul never dies. Those who have departed have merged with the Divine, and their souls are still with you, with us, with the entire nation. Hence we should not sit and shed tears for them, for they are martyrs. Everyone will die, including us. But they have sacrificed their lives to wake us up and make us realize that others should not suffer, that this should not happen again. Know that once you drop the body, there is no more suffering to the soul. However, people who are left behind suffer for their loss. Now this sorrow that you might feel should be channelized properly. Don't give in to depression. We are conducting trauma relief workshops everywhere. All those who saw these attacks, and are suffering with the traumatic impressions it has left in the mind, need to learn pranayama and meditation to flush this negativity out. So ensure that all those who are feeling dejected and scared attend these trauma relief camps and learn meditation so that they can once again be filled with hope, enthusiasm and happiness.

Rest of the World

Beslan Massacre

> Service is an expression of love. Serve in whatever possible manner you can. Ask yourself how you can be useful to people around you and to the whole world and then your heart would start blossoming.
>
> —Sri Sri Ravi Shankar

Sri Sri has inspired many to go beyond their comfort zones to bring solace and joy to those around them. Not just in India but globally too, the volunteers of the Art of Living bring the healing touch of love to those who have lost their loved ones or been hurt by senseless acts of terrorism.

Within hours of the tragedy of the shooting of school children and their parents in the Beslan School in Russia, Art of Living teachers reached to provide solace to the survivors and the grieving friends and relatives of the victims. The nearby areas (in fact, the whole town and surrounding regions) were sealed off by the Russian Army and government, preventing any movement in or out of the place. Recounts Rakesh Shah, who heads the Art of Living movement in Russia:

> We somehow managed to send a few of our teachers to a place near where the tragedy had occurred. It was almost impossible to get in touch with the surviving children or parents because the Russian government had taken them into protection and completely prevented any NGOs, media, etc., from seeing them. Only official government psychologists were allowed to work with the survivors. So we started to teach the courses to their relatives and friends, and to the people of the city, and of course the army soldiers who were permanently stationed there.
>
> However, nine of the hostages secretly came to us (in absolute anonymity) by word of mouth and we

taught a course to them behind closed doors. They were under shock and reported relief and relaxation after the workshop. Notwithstanding all this, the fact is that in the three months after the tragedy, we realized that the incident had handed out (understandably) a huge psychological shock to the relatives and the people of the city in general. Also, the Russian Army which is posted there is constantly under very high levels of stress because of constant killings and the ongoing warfare. We realized that we needed to organize workshops for them to help deal with the stress that they were undergoing. In all, we taught thirty-one courses, covering a total of 689 people in Beslan and the surrounding areas in Chechnya region. Many of the participants were friends, neighbours and relatives of the victims and came to our courses in a state of shock, trauma and depression.

We also taught Breath-Water-Sound and part I courses to 298 people from the Russian Army, including soldiers and officers. For the children and teenagers, we taught four ART Excel courses covering eighty children, and two courses for young adults in the months that followed. Of course, we were not allowed to teach (or even meet) the child hostages. In fact the children were taken away by the government from Beslan immediately after the incident to a children's centre far away from Beslan, along with their parents, for recuperation and rest. No freelance media or NGOs were allowed anywhere near them. However, we managed to teach a course to the hospital staff and for army psychologists who work in that region. Remember that Beslan was just one incident amidst the large-scale terrorism and violence that's going on in the Chechnya region for many years. Hence the people working here, especially those in the army, hospitals, etc., are under a lot of stress. Feedback from all the courses was very positive and we continue to have more courses in the nearby regions.

More than 1400 children, teachers, doctors, nurses and personnel involved in the Beslan tragedy have since then benefited from the Art of Living course.

9/11

Over the years, whenever tragedy has struck our planet, the volunteers of Art of Living Foundation, together with those of the IAHV, have come together in a spirit of service and solidarity to aid the victims of the capriciousness of nature or man. In the aftermath of the 11 September 2001 attacks—when two aircrafts (United Airlines flight 175 and American Airlines flight 11) crashed into the World Trade Center (WTC) twin towers in New York City, leaving a confirmed 2973 people dead along with the nineteen hijackers—the Art of Living volunteers were one of the first to swing into action.

They gave firefighters at the WTC food and taught them stress-relief exercises. 'I will always remember how this city rallied around its firefighters during this tragedy, but I will also remember the contribution of your group. Your assistance was offered when it was needed most and before it became a popular thing to do. You made a real difference,' wrote James Bossert, Battalion 32 fire chief, to the foundation later.

Within hours of the WTC attacks, Hoffeld, an Art of Living volunteer, had gathered people who had taken the Art of Living Foundation's stress reduction programmes in his neighbourhood and went to work on setting up public trauma workshops and on making hundreds of peanut butter and jelly sandwiches which they brought to the firefighters that day. Recounts Hoffeld:

> All the firefighters were using the Hooper Street station as a staging area. When we showed up with our duffel bags filled with sandwiches, we saw hundreds of firefighters sitting on the curbs and on the closed off

street, looking exhausted. In dealing so thoroughly with the disaster, they had not been able to get any food for their members.

Within a few days, other Art of Living Foundation volunteers from around the country came to help, and workshops to alleviate trauma and stress have since been offered to New Yorkers on an ongoing basis at no charge. To date, over 1000 people have participated in the free trauma relief programmes. Although retrospective analysis has questioned the efficacy of conventional psychotherapy in treating mass trauma within the first weeks of a disaster, The Art of Living part I and Breath-Water-Sound teachers and participants reported that trauma symptoms improved dramatically as the three sample cases below prove.

Case 1: Persistent fear

Ms P., aged twenty-eight, suffered constant panic attacks after witnessing the collapse of the twin towers and having her apartment engulfed in the toxic cloud. She was afraid to be alone, afraid to go out, and felt 'numb, depressed, and paralyzed'. Twelve weeks after the terrorist attack, she took the course on the advice of her therapist. The first sudarshan kriya gave her a feeling of lightness and clarity. During the second, she felt happy and peaceful, as though purified. The course relieved her symptoms and helped her get on with life.

Ms. P. is a recovering alcoholic who was sober for two years before 9/11. When interviewed in 2005, she said that the yoga programmes helped her stay sober and to quit smoking. She still practises pranayama and sudarshan kriya, and is taking advanced courses. She has no PTSD or depression symptoms.

Case 2: Sleepless nights

Ms M., aged forty-eight, could not sleep for more than an hour a night for two weeks after 9/11. She was so groggy that she could not return to work as a waitress. During the first sudarshan kriya, she cried with fear every time she got to the fast breath cycles because they reminded her of how she was breathing while running from the dust cloud, terrified that she would die. The next day, however, she felt peaceful during kriya and finished it feeling happy. That night, she slept for twelve hours.

Case 3: Inability to eat

Ms L. was so nauseated after 9/11 that she could not eat. For three weeks, she vomited every time she tried to eat. The night after her first sudarshan kriya, she was able to hold down a meal. After the second kriya, she felt hungry for the first time in weeks.

'The Art of Living course was a chance to purge the sadness from my system. After doing it, there was real serenity, combined with a feeling of energy,' is what Allan Kristen an attorney from New York had to say.

The Art of Living Foundation was invited to participate in 'Back on Track America', a coalition aimed at getting businesses across America back on track in the post-September 11 business climate. Working in concert with 'Back on Track America' partners such as SBTV, America Online, Amtrak, and others, Art of Living Foundation's team of stress-management specialists took a ride to several cities across America, providing stress-management services to small businesses and their employees.

Says Jane Applegate, CEO and founder, SBTV:

> Life is stressful for all of us these days, and meditation not only helps people deal more effectively with stress and anxiety, it also aids mental clarity and focus— qualities that any business can appreciate. The Art of Living Foundation was at the top of my list ... I know their programmes, I respect their credentials and experience in this area. I'm very pleased to have them as part of this coalition.

Madrid Bombings

On 11 March 2004, the world once again woke up to tragedy, this time in Madrid, Spain. Misguided terrorists had once again inflicted pain, this time in the form of a string of train bombings. These were a series of coordinated bombings in the commuter train system of Madrid, which killed 191 people and wounded over 1700. Witnesses and victims were so traumatized that they could not even cry. Anger and vengeful feelings were common while some people were overwhelmed by depression and shock.

Sylvie Dunand, French therapist and an Art of Living volunteer who organized free post-traumatic stress release courses after the attacks, says: 'I have seen people who could not cry, they where haunted by the images of the tragedy. Many had busted ear drums caused by the explosion. The breathing techniques that we taught helped many victims of 11-M to release their post-traumatic stress.'

'My name is Marta. I lost my uncle in the terrorist attacks. I have a lot of anger inside and want to get rid of it. I can't go on with my normal life,' says a young woman in front of twenty people who are nodding in silence at her confession. It is a group of housewives, students, psychologists, etc. They have come together because they have one thing in common: post-traumatic stress as a result of the terrorist attacks in Madrid. After her confession, which is only one of the painful stories that the bombings have left behind, Marta is ready to overcome the psychological symptoms which thousands of people like her have been suffering from after the tragedy. She wants to get rid of the fear and the anxiety that she feels when she steps into a train, the depression caused by the loss of her uncle, and her inability to sleep. It is in order to help people like these that the Art of Living has conducted several stress relief and trauma relief workshops in Madrid. Breathing techniques and other stress elimination methods were taught to several thousands of people who were directly or indirectly affected by the terror attack. The relief camps seem to have worked for the victims since several of them reported the restoration of placidity and freedom from nightmares and sleeplessness.

South Ossetia

Even as the conflict between Russia and Georgia over the breakaway Ossetia escalated, the Art of Living stepped in to bring solace to people traumatized by the conflict. A team of volunteers from Russia, including doctors and psychologists, worked round-the-clock in Tskhinvali after 20 August 2008.

As this book goes to press, more than 2,35,000 people have benefited from the trauma relief sessions which included breathing techniques and meditation. Russian soldiers and Russian peacekeepers, and South Ossetian peacekeepers who were directly in the line of fire have also attended the sessions.

Despite the fierce fighting between Russian forces and South Ossetian separatists on one side and Georgian forces on the other, the volunteers stayed put and attended to people from all walks of life. The effort has been hailed and supported by the minister of healthcare, South Ossetia and the presidential administration.

In addition, civilians, teachers, school children and doctors who man hospitals in the conflict areas have also benefited from the Art of Living's intervention. Ossetian journalists and staff of the presidential administration have also undergone the programme.

The Art of Living has set up two centres in Tskhinvali where civilians attend relief sessions in the morning and evening.

Since August 2008, the region has been witnessing diplomatic tension and clashes, almost erupting into a war between Georgia and South Ossetia. The ethno-political conflict in South Ossetia, which evolved in 1989, developed into a civil war in 1991–92. Despite numerous peace efforts, the conflict remains unresolved.

Just after the Georgia conflict, as he was delivering a lecture to Nobel Prize winners in Norway, Sri Sri Ravi Shankar stressed upon the power of dialogue in resolving conflicts in the world. This is what Sri Sri said:

> There is a great need for dialogue and for creating mediators. The role of a mediator is vital and he needs to play the role of a catalyst without imposing himself. Stress creates barriers in communication. For any dialogue to happen, a mediator is needed, and it is the skill of the mediator that makes successful dialogues.
>
> Misinformation and rumour campaigns are always involved in a conflict. A mediator needs to listen and create hope among the parties involved. A proper understanding of the situation on the part of the mediator is crucial for preventing the situation from escalating.
>
> Most conflicts are based on identity. We have forgotten that first and foremost, we are all human beings. It is only after *this* identity that other identifications such as religion, nationality and gender follow. We need to move beyond our narrow identities to overcome fear, mistrust and conflict in the post 9/11 scenario. To curb terrorism in the long run, children must be provided a multicultural and multi-faith education.

Chapter Seven

Trauma Healings

Disasters can lead us to feel totally helpless. The personal and economic scars of hurricane Katrina and the tsunami were far from healing when the news about the devastating earthquake in Pakistan and India broke. A photo in a newspaper, a news broadcast or a magazine article can lead us to wonder how we can be of help to the victims. In contrast, the media coverage of the earthquake made me think how quickly the victims of the recent tsunami and hurricane, and their surviving loved ones, family and friends had disappeared from the media. The victims of the other two tragedies were quickly forgotten. But there is one man, Sri Sri Ravi Shankar, who does not forget. He continues to work long after the news is off the front pages of the press. His compassion is limitless.

Earthquake in Pakistan and India

On 8 October 2005, an earthquake measuring 7.6 on the Richter scale caused widespread destruction in the Himalayan region of northern Pakistan and north India. The earthquake took the lives of over 75,000 people. The United Nations reported that four million people were directly affected. In fact, this number is prior to the commencement of winter snowfall in the Himalayan region, when many more are sure to have suffered due to the extreme cold. It is estimated that damages incurred are well over

US $5 billion (300 billion Pakistani rupees). The severity of the damage caused by the quake is attributed to severe up thrust, coupled with poor construction. Most of the affected people lived in mountainous regions with access impeded by landslides that blocked the roads, leaving an estimated 3.3 million homeless in Pakistan. Five crossing points were opened on the Line of Control (LoC) between India and Pakistan to facilitate the flow of humanitarian and medical aid to the affected regions, and international aid teams from around the world came to the region to assist in relief. The Art of Living team of volunteers, along with their sister concern, IAHV, were there to offer a helping hand and set up relief camps immediately on the outskirts of Balakot and in the village of Bela. These had seen extreme devastation and the loss of a majority of the local children, who had perished when their school building collapsed on top of them.

Distributing relief supplies to the victims was especially urgent as they faced the risk of exposure to cold weather due to the region's high altitude and the approaching winter. Relief efforts initially focussed on providing basic amenities like food and shelter to survivors. The volunteers collected and distributed tents, blankets, clothes, food, medicines and vaccines as these were considered the most urgent needs of the people. 'Our volunteers had to carry the relief material and climb up a few kilometres to reach these villages,' said Sanjiv Kakar, programme director of IAHV, who oversaw the relief efforts from Baramullah.

In many areas there was no power or adequate water. In collaboration with other NGOs and the army, the Art of Living volunteers helped to get the water and electricity supplies restored. It was imperative to set up a medical camp as the risk of disease and exposure to freezing temperatures in the mountainous region increased with the onset of winter.

The level of stress experienced by the survivors was tremendous. They had to deal with the loss of their loved ones and their homes, and were under constant stress due to disease and physical discomfort. Art of Living teachers conducted trauma relief programmes for survivors to help them deal with their situation. 'We distributed materials, extricated dead bodies and did whatever we could. Now, we will go back and help bring the people out of depression and trauma,' said team leader Kahlid Wasim. If we go by the experiences of those who did the course, they succeeded in their mission.

'Until we did the breathing exercises, my heart had not stopped pounding ... not since the earthquake. Now, at last, I am at peace; I will tell my neighbours to get enrolled for the course,' says Begum Azie from Shaalkot village, Baramullah, Kashmir.

Ashfaq, aged fifteen, says: 'I used to feel that my brain had stopped working since it had lost its retention power after the earthquake. After doing the course, I feel very fresh and have started thinking about the future.'

Arshad Khan, aged fourteen, hailing from Gabra village has this to say about the course: 'After the quakes, I would wake up with a jolt every morning, with my whole body aching. At night, I used to be very scared of noises and would miss my mother who died in the earthquake. Now I feel relaxed and am no longer afraid of noises.'

Thirteen-year-old Ishfaq Ahmed says, 'I used to be very depressed. All I wanted was to die. There was severe pain in my knees. Now the pain is gone and so have the bad thoughts.'

'When you called us down into the rice fields, I thought it was for food. I was surprised when we did the breathing exercise. There was a ghost in my mind since the earthquake, *bhoot svar*, now my mind is free,' says Zarifa Banu, another beneficiary of the Art of Living course.

I am told that relief work and support programmes have been going on there since then, including vaccinating children, supplying more clothes and conducting trauma relief courses. A long-term strategy of rehabilitation of these devastated communities is in place. There is also an innovative initiative underway, focussing on rebuilding homes using eco-friendly material that stays warm during the bitter winters, is earthquake-proof, easy to build, long lasting and low cost. A local teacher in Bela has been trained to build these homes, and the first two 'eco-dome' homes have been built by him. These homes will now act as a model for others to follow.

In response to the efforts by Art of Living volunteers, villagers have admitted that they felt that life was coming back into their community.

Hurricane Katrina

On 29 August 2005, Hurricane Katrina hit southern Louisiana, forcing millions of people throughout the Gulf Coast region of the United States to leave their homes. Many who left that week would have nothing to return to, for the extent to which this disaster affected the area was unprecedented. Hurricane Katrina, coupled with the subsequent floods, proved to be the deadliest hurricane in the US since the 1928 Okeechobee hurricane. The storm is estimated to have been responsible for losses worth $81.2 billion, making it the costliest natural disaster in the history of the United States. In its wake, neighbourhoods were destroyed and families were scattered, separated and dislocated, and the government was left to tackle an unparalleled tragedy.

Katrina left survivors who were traumatized by the suddenness, sheer unreality and magnitude of the devastation. While about 1500 people perished in the flood, thousands more were battling an internal trauma. The loss of family, shelter, and livelihood led to aftershocks that still continue to grip New Orleans and the surrounding areas. For many, the emptiness of a once vibrant city, coupled with memories of evacuation, was too much to bear. Even upon returning, many people could not cope with driving down the streets and seeing the debris. More importantly, many could not sleep or close their eyes; they had no peace of mind and no security. This is where IAHV sprang into action. While many organizations were providing necessary material and physical relief, IAHV recognized the need to release the trauma, fear and psychological unrest in the minds of the affected people.

Sri Sri Ravi Shankar believes that unless the trauma is released, food and medicines won't work. As long as their minds are full of the terrible tragedy that has befallen them, people can't be at peace and eat or sleep.

Hurricane Katrina survivors need help rebuilding their mental health along with their homes and lives. That's why seventeen teachers trained in a disaster-specific yoga breathing intervention travelled south just days after the storm.

Under the guidance of Sri Sri Ravi Shankar, volunteers from the IAHV and the Art of Living Foundation rallied together to provide an unprecedented wave of love and service to the Katrina evacuees. Volunteers in Houston organized materials and went to the Astrodome to serve food and help organize the evacuees, while volunteers around the country donated money and organized projects to raise funds for the Katrina relief efforts. In that first critical week, IAHV volunteers reached out to approximately 200 children in the relief camps throughout the city of Houston.

Within thirty days, IAHV volunteers were conducting stress and trauma relief workshops for evacuees in Baton Rouge, Houston, Dallas and Austin. Sri Sri flew from India specifically to visit and bring relief to the Katrina evacuees in Austin.

'Essentially, while many people were aware of how to scrub mould off their house, they didn't know how to get negative thoughts out of their mind,' said Sri Sri.

In the aftermath of Katrina, Baton Rouge's population doubled overnight as it received the New Orleans evacuees. The school system, roadways, and businesses were over-taxed. Hence, while the city of New Orleans was still mostly vacant, IAHV sent its volunteers north to Baton Rouge. From October 2005 to January of 2006, IAHV reached out to approximately 200 people in Baton Rouge. The participants went through the Art of Living trauma relief course. Thus, IAHV helped to transform a displaced population into a community.

'The Art of Living course allowed me to release a lot of stress and chaos that I was feeling. It allowed me to go really deep within myself, and it was very peaceful, serene and relaxing,' says Kelly McGuire, a displaced resident of New Orleans.

'The course gave me much more than I expected. I was able to feel free and relaxed and to find some peace where there was none. I had a greater awareness and felt calm—something I didn't think I would ever feel again,' said an anonymous survivor of the hurricane.

Tsunami

The earthquake and tsunami on 26 December 2004 that killed 1,50,000 people across Asia reached from Indonesia, the world's largest Muslim majority nation, to India, the world's most populous Hindu one. It hit Thailand's Buddhist majority and Muslim minority, and this small island country, Sri Lanka, which is mostly Buddhist but has sizeable Hindu, Muslim and Christian populations as well. Across nations and religions, then, there has been a search for answers as to why the tsunami came and whom it struck. Among people of great faith, the tsunami is seen as an act of god, although not one understandable by man.

The waves left in their wake an unprecedented natural catastrophe that led to extraordinary loss of life and economic damage. The earthquake and resulting tsunamis left over 30,974 dead, 4698 missing and 5,53,287 displaced in Sri Lanka alone. One-third of those affected are believed to be children, many of whom have been orphaned. Within three hours of the advent of the tsunami, more than 500 volunteers of the IAHV and Art of Living began direct relief work in the worst-affected areas of India, Indonesia, and Sri Lanka. Volunteers of the foundation from around the world have been supporting the direct relief efforts. IAHV provided around 250 tons of relief supplies and 1,00,000 litres of drinking water to the victims. In coordination with the Aspic Benevolent Foundation for Children, IAHV volunteers have provided food, water, clothing and blankets to the affected children, including setting up a children's camp that houses over 5000 potentially orphaned children. Truckloads of basic amenities such as food and clothing, medicines and tents have been distributed in cities across the country. A fully-equipped team of over forty-five doctors and paramedical practitioners conducted medical camps in Kirinth and Galle. In the weeks following the disaster, they also provided vaccines against water -borne diseases like cholera, typhoid and malaria, and treated those with wound infections. Once the immediate physical needs of the victims were met, the volunteers turned to helping them to cope with the emotional and mental trauma left behind by the tsunami. They organized trauma relief breathing workshops for the survivors to help them cope with the shock and fear.

As her mother looks on in gratitude towards Sri Sri and the knowledge he has brought forth, Selva Rani shares with us her tryst with the tsunami:

> I witnessed, in front of my very eyes, the terrible death of my eight-year-old daughter in the tsunami. The crippling helplessness I experienced as my little girl was swept away to a watery grave while I was forced to watch inertly was more unbearable than any emotional turmoil I could experience. As I dissolved in the disbelief—and consequently the grief—of my irreparable loss, the bare escape from a similar fate of my younger daughter made me paranoid about her safety. As the cruel rumours of another tsunami invoked the same intensity of terror, I could not shut out thoughts of finding my younger daughter hanging on to a tree, crying and bleeding after the water subsided. This led me to become mentally broken, in addition to the emotional turmoil and the physical damage that was already done.

I attended the IAHV BWS workshop for trauma relief on the recommendation of my mother, who had already benefited greatly from the same. I feel as if I have escaped the whirlpool of the chronic depression, uncertainty and fear into which I had sunk after the ordeal. My family members, nearly all of whom are already volunteers of the IAHV programme, are relieved to see the change that has come over me in a matter of days.

The sudarshan kriya has had a cathartic effect on my being and I have been rid of the constant fatigue, restlessness and strain that used to plague me earlier. I am able to cope much better with the demands of my rigorous household work. Even my younger daughter, who had been petrified after her misadventure and who was unable to sleep for weeks after the tsunami, seems to have calmed down since the workshop began. My brother, Nalla Tambi, is the lead youth volunteer and has been instrumental in bringing the workshop to his friends and other survivors.

This is what Samundeeshwari has to say about the programme:

I was working as a nurse's assistant at a local hospital before the fateful day on which my entire life was literally washed away in a single stroke. Mother of two, I escaped the wrath of the tsunami by hanging onto the branch of a tree. Convinced that I was going to die, my only thoughts in those moments of abject terror were of my children. After the waves had subsided, I spent the longest eight hours of my life in trying to find them. Stumbling through the wreckage of destroyed houses crawling with sea animals and littered with dead bodies, the macabre journey drove me to the brink of a complete nervous breakdown.

It was in this high strung emotional state that I first came to the IAHV Art of Living BWS workshop. I was also suffering from ill-health owing to the injuries sustained in the tsunami. A highly emotional woman by nature, I was prone to habitual fits of crying. The simple yet powerful breathing exercises coupled with chanting helped me gain control over my erratic mental pattern. The yogic asanas succeeded in normalizing my chronic blood pressure trouble and physically strengthening me. As I did the sudarshan kriya, I felt the haunting emotional insecurity finally drain out of me.

As Samundeeshwari talks about her plans of getting other women she knows to attend the workshop, it is perceptible that in the midst of what is probably the worst destruction we have ever known, her cup of strength runneth over.

Sri Sri, on his visit to Sri Lanka soon after the tsunami to oversee the work being done by his volunteers and to bring solace to those who suffered due to this huge disaster, donated Rs 1.5 billion ($34 million) through his Art of Living Foundation towards relief operations in Sri Lanka and India.

He met the prime minister of Sri Lanka, Mahnida Rajapakse and discussed the modalities of immediate relief and long-term rehabilitation of the victims. The foundation is planning to set up orphanages and homes for destitute women in the affected areas in Sri Lanka and India. A 200-bed residential orphanage and children's home along with an educational complex is under construction in Wellawaya, one of the most economically-backward areas of south-east Sri Lanka. This facility will address the needs of quality primary education and will house 200 orphaned children. Already constructed is a nursery school for the tsunami-displaced children in Karaveddy, Jaffna district. Emphasis in the nursery school will be not only on learning the basic subjects and languages along with different recreational and creative activities, but also on developing human values and creating a sense of belongingness with the world and respect for nature. The education imparted to the children will develop their self-esteem and pride in themselves.

The Art of Living also organized a large refugee camp in Port Blair, Andamans, taking care of the immediate needs of those affected in that region.

In India, the worst hit areas were Nagapattinam and Cuddlore in Tamil Nadu. The district collector, Tenkasi S. Jawahar, praised the efforts of the foundation in the relief work. 'Many NGOs took care of the food and material needs of the tsunami victims. But organizations like the Art of Living helped the victims deal with the mental trauma,' Jawahar said.

Recounting the time when she took up the course, Jayanti says:

> I feel extraordinarily lucky to have not lost any family member, considering the statistics of the district. I can still recall the scenes of death and destruction in my village and many others. Shocked and distressed at the scale and suddenness of the tragedy, I had spent many weeks in an inert state of fear and consequently suffered from physical and mental ill-health. Added to this was the unfulfilled desire to be of help to the stricken survivors that made me feel utterly helpless. I was suffering from acute mental agitation and physical weakness due to a build-up of stress in my system.
>
> When I heard about the IAHV Breath-Water-Sound workshop for trauma relief, I was more than eager to attend. The very first day, I remember, my body felt as though it had relaxed fully for the first time in years. The utter peace of mind I experienced left me amazed and delighted. After doing the sudarshan kriya, I felt that I had been reborn.

Having witnessed perhaps the worst natural disaster in human history, her life now holds meaning and faith that equals the tragedy that she survived. This is what Devi has to share with us:

> I was braving the heat inside a local bus when the first wave of the tsunami hit. I was caught in the second

wave and thrown into the torrent. Paralyzed with shock and fear, I lapsed into unconsciousness. Waking up, I left the hospital I was admitted to in a state of severe physical damage, panicking about the whereabouts of my family. Reaching my village, I was met with the gruesome spectacle of an array of corpses in various states of disfigurement. I stumbled about in fright on the streets for hours, discovering dead bodies of neighbours and friends, and my own house completely destroyed. Even though I was finally reunited with my family, the traumatic search in the village and the sheer panic and shock of not knowing whether I would see them or their lifeless bodies had taken its toll on me. Even weeks later, I felt the same intensity of terror, added to which was the anxiety of the future as the enormity of the loss of home and hearth gradually unfolded its true proportions. I recall the time when I was constantly blaming god, blaming nature and was unable to understand and accept the situation. Accepting material relief from the various institutions working for the survivors was even more painful as it forcefully reminded me that I was now dependent on 'aid' from outside. I often felt depressed and ashamed thinking that from a bright, educated girl, I would be now forced to beg for help.

With a shy smile, Devi tells us about the poem that won her the first prize in Nagapattinam district, maintaining that calamity made her a poet. Her poems, she thoughtfully observes, have reflected the change in her mental state and witnessed a definite upswing in mood after the workshop. She says:

Besides grasping my own emotional and mental mechanisms with ease now, the strength I have found in myself has kindled in me the desire to extend service to my people and my society. The healing and transformation I have observed in my friends, relatives and other survivors struggling with trauma have spurred me to assume the responsibility of bringing the same

relief and knowledge to others around me. For this, I
am working towards arranging workshops in areas that
have not yet been catered to.

Devi is a young third-year college student who survived the
tsunami and went on to become a young seva warrior of the
Art of Living. As this renewed young damsel walks away with
a smile, she leaves behind the lingering fragrance of a sacred fire
burning with power and suppleness, reaching out to the divine
in each one of us.

'Whoever is born on this planet should come for this course ... '
is how Arul, a young fisherman, shows his appreciation for the
trauma relief course conducted in his village after the tragedy.
Elaborating on his point, this is what Arul told us:

Even weeks after the tsunami subsided, I was far too
fearful of the sea to return to fishing. I remember being
so disturbed that I was contemplating migrating to any
nearby town and working as a labourer. Physically, I felt
exhausted all the time and experienced heaviness in my
limbs. The severe mental stress that I was under led to
disorders in my digestive system and caused acute pain
in my back and shoulders. This effectively curtailed my
ability to earn my livelihood.

Initially, my intense mistrust and insecurity made
me sceptical about taking the Breath-Water-Sound
workshop. In fact, I went to the workshop thinking
that I would quit if I did not like the session on the first
day. However, my doubts evaporated on the very first
day when I experienced a deep sense of restfulness after
a long time and decided to finish the full workshop.
After the meditation, I experienced a tangible reversal
in my attitude—from fatalistic negativity to hope and
responsibility. I felt optimistic for the first time after
the catastrophe and my increased energy and zeal
made me want to take a greater part in shouldering
the responsibility of rehabilitation. In fact, after the
sudarshan kriya, I felt so free from fear and scepticism

that I did not fear the threat of another tsunami, confident that I would not only survive the situation but handle it well.

As my physical ailments healed, my mind functioned with unprecedented clarity. I pushed many amongst my fellow survivors to attend the workshop and refused to rest until all the residents of my village had done the course.

Thamayanthi is a full-time IAHV youth volunteer. She tells us her story of moving from weakness to strength as a living proof of what Sri Sri Ravi Shankar often says, 'The more you give, the more strength will be given to you.'

I was a college student when I met with the accident that changed my life. I developed a lasting back pain even after my fractures healed, and suffered from persistent headache and breathing problems. After doing the sudarshan kriya, I experienced immediate relief and went on to do the advanced course which greatly improved my physical condition.

I was so inspired by my own experience that I decided to become a means of bringing this knowledge to others in my community and society. With this determination, I completed the Art of Living YLTP and went on to become a 'Yuvacharya' (volunteer youth leader). For the last three years, I have been dedicated to the goal of reaching out to people in cities and villages with this awareness. At present, along with a team of devoted volunteers, I am working towards bringing much-needed solace and rehabilitation to the survivors of the tsunami in Nagapattinam, My experience in this difficult endeavour has been tough but fulfilling. I remember the cold reception of the IAHV team by the sceptical and grief-stricken villagers which transformed into tears of gratitude and relief once they had attended the workshop. Today, I have fostered warm relations with the villagers and have also been able to ensure that they maintain good relations amongst themselves.

The simplicity and strength that this frail-looking young woman exudes is in itself a source of solace and inspiration to many others.

The Art of Living has undertaken the construction of ninety-four houses in Tamil Nadu's tsunami-ravaged Periyamanickapangu village with the support of the Times Foundation. The uniqueness of this project is that the houses have been built on the very spot where the victims lost their homes.

Risking their own lives, Sri Sri's volunteers have tended to the mental and emotional needs of victims. Apart from supplying immediate material needs, attending to the trauma of the survivors is one of the main targets of the volunteers. Daniel Lac, a BBC reporter who visited Nagapattinam at the time of the disaster had this to say: 'The Art of Living volunteers were singing songs, chanting a few Hindu mantras and singing Christian hymns. Basically can the courses encompass all religions and help people to stop dwelling on the horror that they've been through ... and I saw faces light up in front of me.'

Sri Sri's volunteers are still engaged in trauma relief and long-term rehabilitation of the victims of the 2004 tsunami in Sri Lanka and Nagapattinam, India. Over 50,000 victims have overcome the trauma of the disaster, thanks to Sri Sri's specially- designed stress elimination techniques. Every day, these volunteers set out as true warriors of light, bringing sorely needed comfort and guidance during this difficult time of picking up the pieces and starting all over again. Every day, they devote themselves afresh to the cause of reconstruction and rehabilitation, always mindful of the need for mental and emotional relief before anything else.

Even as the list of amazing personal transformation grows longer with every workshop, the IAHV and Art of Living Foundation continue their tireless mission to bring hope and meaning back into the lives of those who have lived to tell the tale of one of the most horrifying natural disasters of this century.

Flood Victims in Bihar

On 1 September 2008, as the Indian state of Bihar was reeling under the worst floods in fifty years, the Art of Living Foundation mobilized relief material worth Rs 10 crores through its volunteer network throughout the country. It also raised another Rs 40 crores for the rehabilitation of the flood victims.

Appealing to people to donate generously to help the victims, Sri Sri said, 'At the time of such a national calamity, it is our duty to help the people of Bihar and exhibit the innate human value of love, compassion and service.'

A team of volunteers, including doctors, reached the affected areas within hours and began providing relief to the victims. Based on the feedback from the volunteers on the field, items which were urgently needed for the relief operations were dispatched.

The organization also launched massive collection drives to solicit support from all sections of society. Clothes, water purifying machines that could operate without electricity or battery, food and medicines, plastic sheets, candles, clothes, boats, life-jackets, life-saving ropes, etc., were sent to the worst-affected districts of Arariya, Madhyapura and Supoul. Apart from ensuring emergency supplies, the Art of Living also conducted trauma relief workshops in partnership with UNICEF.

Farmer Suicides in Vidarbha

> Service is to see what is needed, and be available for the surrounding circumstances. It is the willingness to jump in and be available to the situation.
>
> —Sri Sri Ravi Shankar

Over the past few years, the Vidarbha region of Maharashtra has been making headlines for all the wrong reasons: first, due to the growing number of farmer suicides, and then owing to an outbreak of life-threatening chikungunya.

The failure of monsoons in this part of western India caused a decline in the production of cotton, the cash crop of the region. Add to that some lopsided government policies and red-tapism, and you have the perfect recipe for disaster.

Though reluctantly, the state government did acknowledge that farmers in the region were a worried lot. Over 1800 farmers had committed suicide by then. The worst-affected areas were Yavatmal, Amaravati, Akola, Washim, Buldhana and Wardha.

Our story is all about an experiment called the Art of Living. Exactly a year ago, when Art of Living started its activities in Morshi tehsil of Amravati district—one of the worst affected by farmer suicides—it drew sneers. The state government was criticized for forcing distressed farmers to a stiff dose of spiritualism to cover up its failures and in an effort to curtail the alarming rate of suicides among farmers in the cotton belt of the region.

Despite criticism, the Art of Living started Project Vidarbha-Swavalamban programme along with the YLTP. It continued with its efforts to spread positive attitude among farmers. Starting with a fifty-strong team of youth leaders drawn from various parts of Maharashtra, the Art of Living Foundation conducted basic courses for villagers. At the same time, it trained them on new farming techniques. This apart, camps were conducted to teach them skills such as chemical-free farming, zero-budget farming, animal husbandry and rainwater harvesting.

Continuing to this day, the programme assists them in conserving rainwater through soak pits. It has also revived the age-old farming technique of using compost for crops instead of the more expensive pesticides and fertilizers. This is being done to reduce the input cost for the crops.

Besides helping out the farmers, the programme also seeks to create better living conditions for the villagers and to empower women through vocational courses. In a nutshell, it seeks to address the farmers' financially-unviable farming techniques, along with treating their psychological breakdown. Sensing a ray of hope, over 507 villages are taking advantage of the programme today.

In these villages, the mornings begin with the village folk gathering for breathing exercises and meditation under the supervision of the Yuvacharyas. The course has strengthened the sense of belonging and community among the villagers. In fact, Sri Sri, during his visit to Vidarbha, had inspired the people to support each other during these trying times. 'Committing suicide is foolishness. It offers no solutions to any problems. If one family has no food and the neighbour has enough to survive for two days, the latter should offer help without hesitation. The country's progress has suffered due to party and caste divisions. Do away with all such inhibitions and help the needy,' he said.

The farmers who have successfully come out of depression and suicidal tendencies interacted with Sri Sri and thanked him for giving them hope when all seemed to be lost due to successive crop failures in the region.

They said that Project Vidarbha-Swavalamban programme and YLTP have not only boosted their morale, but also helped them in equipping themselves with techniques and skills to cure the malaise of suicides. 'The Art of Living has changed our lives for the better,' says Anand Amrute of Nimdhi village in Amravati district. 'I have given up all vices. My health has improved. I was overweight; thanks to the sudarshan kriya, I have lost 10 kg.'

His nineteen-year-old son, Kalpesh, has enrolled for the YLTP. Amrute has stopped using chemical fertilizers in his three-acre farm and is instead using the vermi-compost technique he learnt at the camp. 'Over 500 people from Nimdhi have taken to the Art of Living way of life. Most people have stopped drinking and other vices. This has brought about a tremendous change in family life. Family disputes and stress have reduced and people have found peace,' Amrute informs us.

'There hasn't been a single instance of suicide in the 151 villages we have worked in so far, which is in complete contrast to the time when all seemed lost with one farmer committing suicide every eight hours,' says Vijay Hakay, who is coordinating the initiatives. The project has certainly restored normalcy to the lives of farmers and relieved them of trauma. Art of Living has given people a new lease of life, especially to the youth who are developing into young men who are strong, both mentally and physically, and able to serve the society at large.

The Downtrodden of the Earth

The caste system has been the most misunderstood and the most vilified aspect of Indian society. It was originally an arrangement for the distribution of functions in society, a bit like the guilds we had in Europe in the Middle Ages. But as Sri Aurobindo points out: 'There is no doubt that the institution of caste degenerated. It ceased to be determined by spiritual qualifications, which were once essential, and came to be moulded by the purely material tests of occupation and birth.'

Today, we can see a number of Indian politicians dividing the country on the basis of religion and caste. The caste system has become a tool for getting votes as the lower castes and Muslims constitute nearly 70 per cent of the electorate. Yet, it is also true that unforgivable human rights abuses are carried out in the name of the caste system. Though many reformers such as Mahatma Gandhi raised their voices against untouchability, it still prevails in many rural areas of India.

Enter Sri Sri, who feels that although there are many laws in place to protect caste, based violations and discrimination, only a change of heart and mind can bring about the required transformation. He says that there is a need for enlightened citizens from all walks of life to raise a unanimous voice against this social stigma.

In fact, much before the politicians got into the act, Sri Sri was already working towards uniting upper caste Hindus to enter into a dialogue with Dalits. This is why a path-breaking conference was organized in Delhi in 2007, called 'Truth and Reconciliation'. Many social groups and NGOs participated in this historic meeting to bring about change. This conference endorsed a seven-point concrete action plan which will take the message to the whole of India.

One of the most unconstitutional actions of the upper caste Hindus is to not allow Dalits into temples. This is a discrimination that does not have any meaning in a world which has moved beyond segregation on the basis of colour, class or caste. One of the action points that came out of this conference was to work towards doing away with this discrimination. For example, collective celebrations, including community feasts, would bring about better understanding between those that have been opposed to each other for decades.

Apart from this, abolition of separate utensils for Dalits, and empowerment of women from economically weaker sections of society, be they from any caste, were some other things that an agreement was reached on.

As Sri Sri says, 'Education is an essential tool if you aim to work towards an enlightened society.' Providing education facilities, especially to the weaker sections of the society is a must. In fact, Dalit children need to be educated in spiritual and religious studies too—subjects of study that have been denied to them for hundreds of years.

The Indian constitution provides for equality and justice for one and all, without any discrimination, and this should be implemented without delay.

However we should not, at any rate, go to the other extreme of blaming and maligning those who were born into the upper castes. Hindus should not allow the caste system to be used shamelessly against them, as has been done in the last two centuries by religious heads, and by pre- and post-independence Indian politicians to further their own interests.

And what of the much-maligned Brahmins? In the Vedic times, the priests, who acted as the sacrifice-makers and were poets, occultists and yogis, had no other occupation in life and their positions were thus not hereditary but depended on their inner abilities. And it was the same thing with warriors, merchants, and people who were into other professions. 'Even when these classes became hereditary,' remarks Sri Aurobindo in his book *Foundations of Indian Culture*, 'from the king downwards to the Shudra, the predominance, say, of the Brahmins, did not result in a theocracy because the Brahmins, in spite of their ever-increasing and finally predominant authority, did not and could not usurp the political power.' The rishi had a peculiar place: he was the sage, born from any caste, who was often counsellor to the king, of whom he was also the religious preceptor. Look at what happened in France, for instance, where the Church became so rich and powerful that during the French Revolution, the new republic decided to separate the State and the Church.

Another misinformation is that Brahmins are incredibly rich. This has been used by western and Muslim historians to justify the looting and razing of Hindu temples in India. Are Brahmins really that rich? Just look around you today. In fact you might see a lot of Brahmins who are not only poor, but also discriminated against. See the Kashmiri pandits, the original Brahmin community of the Kashmir valley. Nearly 40,000 of them had to flee their ancestral homes under terror and are living today as refugees in their own country. Did you know that you can find Brahmin rickshaw-pullers and coolies in Delhi, with most of them living in slums? Did you know that most of the public toilets in Delhi are cleaned by Brahmins? Or that many priests in some of the small temples survive on a meagre pittance? Despite this, as French historian Alain Danielou wrote, 'The teaching of philosophy, arts and sciences, which constituted the prestigious

Indian cultural tradition, were ignored more and more, and could survive only thanks to the Brahmins, who upheld the traditions without any help whatsoever from the State.'

Sri Sri Ravi Shankar has often expressed concern over the fast-spreading obsession over the issue of reservation. Maintaining that caste-based reservation will not end disparities in society, he said, 'While being born in any a particular caste should not be a curse, reverse discrimination is not the way for justice.'

According to Sri Sri, what India needs is measures that will unite the country and remove inequality at all levels. Reservation on the basis of caste will not only divide the country, but will also hurt the self-esteem of our people. He called upon politicians to stop dividing and discriminating in the name of caste and religion.

Chapter Eight

Prison Healings

For most of us, our only exposure to prisons has been through movies that sensationalize the violence and brutality of prison life, and depict them as concrete houses of pain surrounded by fences of barbed wire. Yet, prisons and correctional institutions are not always the dreaded hotbeds of violence that we imagine them to be. While it's true that there cannot be a fate more wretched than to spend one's life locked in a cell, never seeing the world and knowing full well that one is going to die there, the experience of coming face-to-face with yourself with nothing to distract you can also be a grace, and can help one come closer to god. Sri Aurobindo, who spent a year in Alipore jail during the struggle for India's independence, spoke about his experience thus:

> The agnostic was in me, the atheist was in me, the sceptic was in me and I was not absolutely sure that there was a god at all. But now all was changed ... I have spoken of a year's imprisonment. It would have been more appropriate to speak of a year's living in an ashram. The only result of the wrath of the British government was that I found god.

Sri Sri's Prison SMART programme was developed specially for the high-stress environments of jails and juvenile detention centres, with the underlying principle that every culprit is but a victim of his or her circumstances. As Sri Sri says, 'If we examine our own lives, we will discover that there is nothing we ourselves have not done, no sin we haven't committed during our many incarnations. That will stop us from judging and condemning the men and women in prison who are also our brothers and sisters.'

The work done in prisons by Art of Living teachers, both in India and abroad, is nothing short of amazing. It is not possible to mention all the names here, but there are several prisons that have undergone a veritable revolution of love and change, thanks to the sudarshan kriya.

The story of Sajjan from Haryana is an account of self-discovery and profound change after participating in the course. In his own words:

> As long as I can remember, I have always been restless, footloose and fancy-free. Although I had a keen and sharp mind, I did not enjoy school and refused to study beyond Class VIII. My father was a policeman but I did not wish to follow in his footsteps; so he sent me to train at an automobile workshop. I stayed there for three years, learning the trade, but the grease and the grime soon got to me and I quit. I wanted to make a lot of money, fast.
>
> I opened a dairy farm, cutting corners in whatever ways I could to make the business thrive. After a successful run, it started showing losses, but I bailed out just as quickly and moved on to the transport business. This too did well for some time but again, as soon as a problem showed up, leading to some downslide in business, I just wanted to move on.
>
> I went to the Middle East for four years and did all kinds of odd jobs. On my return, my father, who had retired by now, asked me to join the family business of financing and making passports. Business picked up and my mind, as usual, was in overdrive. I would go to any lengths to make a quick buck, wining, dining and entertaining clients just so that good business came my way.
>
> My rapid rise had made me very arrogant. I was at

a point in my life where I felt I could do anything, and that nothing and nobody could stand in my way. It was then that that fateful event occurred.

Once I sat drinking with a group of friends till late in the night. Among my companions was an assistant commissioner of police who had often turned a blind eye to my activities in return for the commissions I gave him. That night he asked me for Rs 1 lakh. When I refused, he threatened me with dire consequences. Tempers rose and an ugly brawl ensued, during which we came to blows. In the ensuing madness, even before I knew it, he lay dead before me by my hand. I was momentarily stunned, but my mind took over and we worked to destroy any evidence of my crime. I was picked up by the police a few days later and brought to Tihar Jail.

Here I continued as unrepentantly as ever. Like a caged lion, I marked out my territory and functioned accordingly. I was chosen to monitor the other inmates in my barrack. The duties on prison campus were allotted to them by me. They all knew that if they got on my wrong side it would be the worse for them. Breaking queues for water, milk, the toilet, etc., was my prerogative. For a long time they all kept quiet, before I became too much and their complaints about me filtered to the higher authorities. I was punished with solitary confinement.

I was 'solitarily' housed in a 10 feet by 10 feet room for the next eight months with seven other inmates. There was one toilet in which we bathed and performed our other bodily functions. The heat and stench in summer was unbearable. Our food was given to us inside the cell and we were allowed to stretch our legs for 15 minutes in the morning and evening. Prior to my confinement, I had enrolled for the Art of Living basic course. It was greed for the home cooked food that the other inmates' relatives brought them that drew me. The place where the course was conducted was right next to it. I always managed my share of the spoils. This was the only reason I had signed up for the course. I did not know what I had done.

Out of sheer boredom and lack of exercise, I started going through the whole session. I did not do everything correctly as prescribed since, during most of the course, my mind was on the food. It was strange, but something seemed to be happening to me ... something that had never happened in all the years of my life. My overactive mind seemed to have calmed down.

I began doing kriya for hours, totally wrapped up in myself, without the need to talk much to my other companions. In fact I was actually deriving so much pleasure from it that my time in solitary confinement became much more bearable. There was a shift within.

Once I was out of the confinement, I signed up for the Art of Living advanced course. The meditation I went through had me spellbound. And I continued my growth further. Getting up at three in the morning, I would begin my inward journey to rest in the quiet within. I would meditate for long hours in the ward with a sheet covering me fully. I think this amazed not just everybody else but even me. From being a terror and a bully, I had become quiet and self-contained. The energies of my mind, now channelized positively, turned towards making the jail a better place for others to live in.

One point that really hit home through the course was that opposing values are complementary in life. If there is an up, there will be a down; we just have to have the staying power to go through with it. Running away and cutting losses is not persevering, which is essential to be a success in any field. I had always wanted everything good too fast and never gone with the flow of a low period with patience.

Although I did not join the SRIJAN (Social Rehabilitation of Inmates in Jail and Aiding the Needy) workshop, I was active in other ways. I started to organize events, follow-ups and the play 'Udisha' by the Art of Living, even taking active part in it. Being a part of the SRIJAN team and acting in it gave me so much self-confidence that I could reflect upon my life and share my previous actions honestly with many. My whole attitude had undergone such a change that I also started taking yoga classes for the inmates on Sampadji's suggestion. Sampadji was another inmate who impressed me greatly by his gentleness and simplicity.

Around this time, my inner journey stood on a wobbly ground as I also nurtured the fear of punishment within me. I had not admitted to my crime so far. The desire to tell the truth rose up in me as I meditated and I asked for god's forgiveness. As this truth of my complete surrender unfolded within me, I felt aglow with this assurance that, come what may, I would be taken care of. I was ready to tell the truth to the judge and for the punishment. It was god's will that would rule my life now. It belonged to him.

Today, although a free man after serving my time, I take full responsibility for my actions and therefore share my story with the world. It was important that I go to jail to serve time and learn discipline through my experiences there. It would have been a total downslide otherwise. If I had not been introduced to these teachings by the Art of Living, I would not have reflected so deeply upon my ways and understood all the places I had gone wrong. I would not have imbibed this education outside and so coming here was a blessing in disguise. I have emerged a different and changed man. I have a decent business now and am following my path as shown to me by Guruji. I thank him for the grace and blessings that I have received from him through sudarshan kriya. I pray that I will be able to serve him better some day.

SRIJAN was started in Tihar Jail, Delhi, and is now functioning in a number of jails in India. It teaches vocational skills to inmates during confinement and empowers them with skills that would make them independent on their release. Tihar Jail, housing

12,000 inmates (some in the high risk category) is one of Asia's largest prisons and is also one of the prison programme's biggest successes. According to Vanika, who has been actively involved with the programme in Delhi, till date, more than 25,000 inmates have benefited from the course. India has the largest base of both prisons and prisoners where the Prison SMART programme has been conducted. It has been conducted in 100 prisons, touching the lives of 52,000 inmates across the nation. Many states, for example, West Bengal, Jammu and Kashmir, Bihar and Gujarat have tied up with the Art of Living to conduct the programme in all their jails and correction homes. According to the Art of Living statistics, nearly 3550 prisons are participating in this programme on a regular basis.

Since 1992, this programme has reached out, touched and transformed the lives of 1,20,000 inmates in incarceration facilities across the globe. It aids angry, depressed, troubled and stressed and even drug dependent individuals to take charge of their lives and to regain their self-esteem as some of these testimonies bear witness. (Some of the names have been deleted to protect the identity of the individuals.)

Police forces around the world face the consequences of the stress they are exposed to in the line of duty. Police officers who are under stress are overburdened, which makes it difficult for them to focus on their work. The fire power which is given to police officers needs to be used with great care. This is possible only when the personnel are free from stress. Officers under stress can and do misuse their power over those in their care, like Ulrich who was terrorized during his time in jail in Germany:

> I was accused of stealing and thus came about my imprisonment. In a moment, my life changed. I became a slave to one feeling—fear. I was frightened and had terrifying visions of what they might do with me. I was desperately looking for a direction to come out of it. When I got the opportunity to do the basic course, I embraced it with the urgency with which one would

embrace a life-jacket in the swirling seas. So deep was the effect of the course that I immediately took the advanced course too. Now I no longer know fear. I have found the confidence to live, no matter what I have to go through. Who am I to judge the fairness of what happened to me? I have accepted the inevitability of the situation and, in doing so, I have broken past the iron bars which were trapping my soul. I have found a new direction in life. With whatever I have gained from the course, both emotionally and spiritually, my strongest desire is to be a part of the organization and to serve humanity.

Kiran Bedi is one of the most dynamic and forthright police officers I have met. It was her drive that led to the transformation of the Tihar Jail into 'Tihar Ashram' during her tenure there. It was on her initiative that holistic techniques like meditation, pranayama and yoga were first introduced as tools of change for the prisoners to transform into better citizens of the globe.

When she was joint commissioner of the Police Training College in Delhi, she introduced this programme there with the belief that it is important to train the police to be humane towards prisoners in order to be able to help reform them. She says:

Prison training was conducted for the Delhi Police Training College with the idea of getting the police to learn how to manage stress and deal with offenders in a humane way. The results were impressive. The relationship between the offenders and police became cordial and inspiring rather than frightening.

This example has been replicated in many jails not only in India but around the world like in Russia, Germany, South Africa, the UK and the US with great success. The benefits seen were far-reaching, as research shows. In the US, research done in the prisons has been an eye-opener:

- 80 per cent of the inmates reported a full night's sleep after the course.
- 60 per cent of the prisoners reported that they felt less aggressive towards the staff and fellow inmates.
- There has been a measurable and sustained reduction in feelings of violence, anger, rebelliousness, depression, fear, and feelings of isolation in those who participated in the course.
- There has been a marked reduction in recidivism, i.e., the continual return of inmates to the jail.
- The police found that after regular practice, there was a marked improvement in the relations between the police and the prisoners, with a better understanding and cooperation of the prisoners, not only with the authorities but also among themselves.

The following statements bear witness to the above research. John H. was at the end of his tether when he did the Prison SMART programme. This is what he had to share with us:

> I was feeling suffocated in the prison. Feelings of guilt, persecution and depression kept growing more and more intense. I wanted to hang myself and end my life, but couldn't find a place or means to do it. I even tried with my pyjamas. I felt like a complete failure in every way and could only despair at the years ahead, which would have the same misery in store for me. I used to stay in ward number ten. I remember that I was very tense and upset on the day when it was announced that the Art of Living course was to commence. I decided to join. After completing the course, everything changed. I can now sleep well at night. I have become energetic and feel the inclination to talk pleasantly to people. There is a new-found will to live. I do not know what life has in store for me, but I am ready for it. It is no longer a source of dejection for me.

Harry H. testifies:

> I had been looking for a chance to get out of jail so that
> I could get even with fate. I had been made to suffer. I
> wanted revenge for that. Had I not taken this course,
> I would probably have committed at least fifty more
> murders. I would most likely have ended up a sorry mass
> of flesh and blood, killed in an encounter by the police.
> But the course made me realize that I too am a human
> being. Earlier, I used to view myself as a doomed devil, a
> predestined sinner. That was my only identity. But during
> the course, I met myself as a human being—only and
> purely a human being. The oppressive hunger for revenge
> has been replaced by the joyous desire to spread love.

One of the most telling effects of the sudarshan kriya is an
impulse to forgive, as experienced by Mari N:

> I was growing to be an extremely vindictive person. I
> resented my life and wished the worst for those who
> had got me into prison. But after the Art of Living
> course, my way of thinking has taken a turn. Now I
> am in a state where I can forgive my foes. Rather, I am
> thankful to them that they brought me to this juncture
> in my life where I got the opportunity to transform my
> way of thinking. An incident can only be a trigger point
> to reveal one's basic weaknesses. My punishment did
> not create my faults. I cannot justify my feelings and
> attribute them to my imprisonment. In fact I feel grateful
> that I was pushed into a situation which brought out all
> my hidden flaws. They were put in motion and aroused
> enough to be dealt with through the power of the kriya.
> Since then, there has been a remarkable change in my
> attitude, the most significant of which is my readiness
> to forgive.

After doing your time in prison, it is never easy to come out
and re-integrate into society. There is always this feeling of
guilt, even if you've 'done your time', and uncertainty about the

reaction of people. After leaving prison, many prisoners feel lost and fall prey to their old habits. However, it has been seen that those inmates who had done the Prison SMART course were more confident and ready to start life in a positive manner, with dignity. Armed with the knowledge of the Self, they know that it is possible to walk out of prison as better human beings with their head held high.

Anonymous inmate of a prison in the USA:

> I was a prisoner amidst strangers—perhaps not strangers, because we did appear to share a common fate. Nevertheless, I was consumed by loneliness and dejection. There was no purpose to my days and I could not even breathe freely. I was ready to try anything to feel better. When I experienced the power of the sudarshan kriya and the pranayama, I felt revitalized and fresh. It was as if the clouds had evaporated and I was cleansed by light, clean rain. I do my kriya regularly. If I feel lazy or dull, the sudarshan kriya immediately makes me feel better.

A jail inmate in Pakistan:

> Assalamwalekum! My name is Noor Sarwar. My wife and I are here as undertrials. Life had come to a stop as we awaited the verdict. Hope was diminishing and anxiety had become the all-encompassing emotion that dictated our lives. When I heard about the Art of Living course, I felt curious to know more. So I decided to take the course. It did not touch me the first day, but by the end of the second day, I was completely under its spell. The transition from hopelessness to quiet peace was almost magical. I had rediscovered the miracle of life. Since then, my mind has been fresh and awake. I no longer feel my problems tying me down. I am happy now and mingle well with people.

A female inmate from a prison in Canada:

> I was driven by hatred, hatred for the people who were responsible for my imprisonment, hatred for my family who despised me, hatred for every soul who enjoyed freedom while I was trapped behind bars. Now I am happy and can focus on my daily prayers. A lot of my anger has been eliminated. Earlier I used to think that when I get out of prison, I'll avenge my suffering by inflicting pain on others. I used to question why this has happened to me. But it is not so any more. In fact, now I think that coming to jail was a fortunate misfortune.

Conclusion: The Miracle of the Grace

'We cannot see God,' wrote Sri Aurobindo, 'because of his workings and especially because he works in us through our nature and not by a succession of arbitrary miracles. Man demands miracles so that he may have faith; he wishes to be dazzled in order that he may see.'

For many, the presence of Sri Sri Ravi Shankar works miracles. The amazing grace that flows through him brings about a complete transformation of both the mind and the body. And isn't breathing itself the greatest miracle? Indeed, to breathe joyfully is to breathe in freedom, to surrender to life itself. Writes Mark, an Art of Living volunteer:

> I attended three advanced courses. The first couple of times, I enjoyed the silence, the yoga and the breathing, but I could not understand why people were so devoted to Guruji. Things changed during the third course. My instructor's talk on surrender got me thinking, as did the fact that I have had a question mark around faith for some years now. During the three-hour meditation on a Saturday, my leg became incredibly sore and, remembering what my instructor had said about surrender, I asked Guruji to help me as I couldn't focus. My call was answered and I had the most beautifu, hollow and empty meditation. After finishing the meditation, I was asked to go and be with nature.
>
> It was warm and sunny outside and I lay down on my back on the grass near the creek. As I lay there, my

arms started tingling, vibrating. I felt a connection and couldn't help but laugh out loud—it was an amazing feeling. Later on, in the next break before dinner, when I lay back and looked at the sky, I could see what I can only assume was energy moving around. It was like little bright sparks dancing all over the sky.

Throughout the day, I surrendered two or three times and had that feeling of having fallen in love. When you meet someone and you know they are the person for you ... *that* is how I feel for Guruji.

Surrender is indeed the most difficult thing to do, especially for a person like me, whose very education has been all about having control over one's life and mind. But then what is control? Control over one's thoughts, emotions and actions is but an illusion. In South Indian Vaishnavite temples, there is a daily ritual by which you are crowned, quite literally, when you bow low and surrender in front of the deity. The priests place a beautiful crown made of pure silver called the 'shadaari' on your head. If you have been thus crowned, it symbolizes that you have surrendered. 'Once we learn to surrender,' says Sri Sri, 'love happens.'

Love and gratitude are feelings oft expressed by those whose lives have been touched by Sri Sri Ravi Shankar. He is someone who has devoted his entire life to bringing peace and love to a world full of hatred, war and conflict. All religions say the same thing—that we should be on the path of truth, compassion and humanity. Why then is there a need for conflict? The means to bring peace is to open our hearts and to listen and accept each other. When our message is pure and our intentions clear, then it is only a matter of time before harmony is established amongst people.

As Sri Sri often says, 'The wise and intelligent do not fight; it is the ignorant who wage war. There is love in each heart and we must recognize and honour the truth that it is this love that manifests itself in different hearts as different religions.

Spirituality is like the ocean and religion is like a river whose sole purpose is to flow into that selfsame ocean.'

We seek unity amongst our ilk only when we are free of stress. In fact there is no need to even 'seek' this unity, because the reality is that we are all one anyway. What we need to do is wipe away that film of dust called stress that has settled over us. We can smile in life only when we realize that we are one. Religion should bring a smile on your face and joy in your life. The need of the moment is to spread love and this is the responsibility that we all have to undertake.

Healing one's mind begins with the process of recognizing the naturalness of the path to the Divine. As Art of Living practitioner, Daniel, puts it:

> This course has taken me into an appreciation of my own mind. I no longer make excuses for myself such as, 'Oh, this path will work for so and so, but not for me because ...' I now recognize the connectedness I have with the Divine, and have the ardent desire to do all I can to strengthen this connection using the virtues god has given me. I am now aware of my own obsessions. Now whenever I catch myself underestimating my own strength, I understand that it is not me, but the Divine that is responsible for the outcome. I can't tell you what a shift this is for me who was so driven a person.

Faith is essential for healing to happen, and for grace to flow. So how do we foster unshakeable faith? The secret lies in cultivating a faith that is based on absolute understanding, dedication and selflessness, rather than on relative existence or events—in the spirit of 'come what may, it does not matter'. This one thought is enough to make your faith in the self and the infinite existence both stronger and deeper.

In Sanskrit, a disciple is also called *Anthavasi*, or 'someone who dwells inside the guru'. This implies that it is not only the guru who resides within the heart of the disciple but also the disciple who lives in the heart of the master. They are one. The love of the master surrounds you all the time. When you become aware of this, you become a devotee. When you experience this all-encompassing, unconditional love, then you need nothing more. No lack remains in your life. The relationship between the guru and *shishya* is unique. Those who are fortunate to have found this relationship have experienced the ultimate connection that puts an end to individual separation, misery and smallness of the mind. The guru is not just a body; he is beyond the body; he is spirit, space and the vastness of life. The unique relationship between the shishya and the guru takes us beyond ourselves to experience and touch the Divine through the grace of the guru.